Merry Christmas,

THE BIG BOOK
OF WILD ANIMALS

THE BIG BOOK OF WILD ANIMALS

COMPILED AND EDITED BY

MARGARET GREEN

PICTURES BY

JANUSZ GRABIANSKI

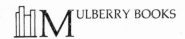 MULBERRY BOOKS

Library of Congress Catalog Card Number: 63-7132

Editorial arrangement and commentary © 1964 by
Margaret Green

Illustrations copyright © 1964 by Carl Ueberreuter
Druck und Verlag (M. Salzer), Vienna, Austria

Printed in Austria

SBN 531-02052-5

ACKNOWLEDGMENTS

The editor and the publisher have made every effort to trace the ownership of all material contained herein. It is their belief that the necessary permissions from publishers, authors, and authorized agents have been obtained in all cases. In the event of any questions arising ˀs to the use of any material, the editor and publisher, while expressing regret for any error unconsciously made, will be pleased to make the necessary correction in future editions of this book.

The stories reprinted in this book are used by permission and special arrangements with the proprietors of their respective copyrights, who are listed here.

Thanks are due to the following authors, publishers, publications, and authorized agents who helped make this collection possible:

"The Presumptuous Tiger" from *Bandoola* by J. H. Williams. Copyright © 1953 by J. H. Williams. Reprinted by permission of Doubleday & Co., Inc.

"Shag: Last of the Plains Buffalo" from *Shag: Last of the Plains Buffalo* by Robert McClung. Copyright © 1960 by Robert M. McClung. Reprinted by permission of William Morrow and Company, Inc.

"Tiger Cub Prisoners" from *Wild Life in the Jungle* by C. Bernard Rutley. Reprinted by permission of Macmillan & Co. Ltd., London.

"Beaver Lodge Visitors" from *A Beaver's Story* by Emil E. Liers. Copyright © 1958 by Emil E. Liers. Reprinted by permission of The Viking Press, Inc.

"Seal Games" from *Scaf the Seal* by Lyda (Père Castor). Reprinted by permission of George Allen & Unwin, Ltd., London.

"The Red Enemy" from *Sajo and her Beaver People* by Grey Owl. Copyright © 1938 by Grey Owl. Reprinted by permission of Charles Scribner's Sons of New York, N. Y.; The Macmillan Company of Canada Limited; and Peter Davies Ltd., London.

"The Blasted Pine" from *The Devil of the Woods* by Paul Annixter. Copyright © 1958 by Paul Annixter. Reprinted by permission of Hill and Wang, Inc.

"Stripes, The Unconcerned" from *Jim, The Story of a Backwoods Police Dog* by Major Charles C. D. Roberts. Copyright © 1929 by The Macmillan Company. Reprinted by permission of Lady Joan Roberts.

"A Man-made Water Hole" from *Adventures in the African Jungle* by Mary L. Jobe Akeley. Copyright © 1930 by Mary L. Jobe Akeley. Reprinted by permission of Dodd, Mead & Company, Inc., New York.

"A Pair of Kings" from *Strange Animals I Have Known* by Raymond Lee Ditmars. Copyright © 1931 by Raymond L. Ditmars. Reprinted by permission of Harcourt, Brace & World, Inc., New York.

"The Red Ghost" from *Unsere Freunde, die Tiere* by Svend Fleuron. Reprinted by permission of Eugen Diederichs Verlag, Düsseldorf, W. Germany.

"The Playful Lions" from *I Married Adventure* by Osa Johnson. Copyright © 1940 by Osa Johnson. Reprinted by permission of J. B. Lippincott Co., Philadelphia.

"Boomer, a Kangaroo" from *Boomer* by Denis Clark. Copyright © 1955 by The Viking Press, Inc. Reprinted by permission of The Viking Press, Inc., New York.

"Firepoint" from *Romances of the Wild* by H. Mortimer Batten. Reprinted by permission of the executors of the late H. Mortimer Batten.

"The Battle of the Fangs" from *White Fang* by Jack London. Published by permission of Irving Shepard.

"The Story of a Red Deer" from *The Story of a Red Deer* by J. W. Fortescue. Reprinted by permission of Capt. J. H. Carew. M. C.

"Mostly Monkeys" from *The Overloaded Ark* by Gerald Durrell. Copyright © 1953 by Gerald M. Durrell. Reprinted by permission of The Viking Press, Inc., New York.

"The Elephants' Dance" from *Toomai of the Elephants*, in *The Jungle Book*, by Rudyard Kipling. Reprinted by permission of Mrs. George Bambridge and Doubleday and Company, Inc., New York; and the Macmillan Company of Canada Ltd.

"The Lion" from *Lion Hound* by Jim Kjelgaard. Reprinted by permission of Holiday House, Inc., New York.

"Shillings from the Fon" from *The Bafut Beagles* by Gerald Durrell. Copyright © 1954 by Gerald M. Durrell. Reprinted by permission of The Viking Press, Inc., New York.

"Tom, the Grizzly" from *Tom, the Grizzly* by Olai Aslagsson, Stavanger. Reprinted by permission of the author.

"The Battle with Man" from *The Way of a Lion* by Alden G. Stevens. Copyright © 1939 by J. B. Lippincott Company. Reprinted by permission of J. B. Lippincott Company.

"Grey Shadow, the Wolf" from *Beyond the Timberland Trail* by Joseph Chipperfield. Copyright © 1953 by Longmans, Green & Co., Inc., New York. Reprinted by permission of David McKay Company, Inc., New York.

"Jim's Circus Crocodile" from *Jock of the Bushveld* by Sir Percy Fitzpatrick. Reprinted by permission of Longmans Green & Co. Ltd., London.

"Tarka's Joyful Water-life" from *Tarka the Otter* by Henry Williamson. Copyright © 1960 by Henry Williamson. Reprinted by permission of Brandt & Brandt, New York.

"Foxes at Play" from *A Shepherd's Life* by W. H. Hudson. Reprinted by permission of The Royal Society for the Protection of Birds, and The Society of Authors.

"Something to Grouse About" from *That Rascal, Fridolin* by Hans Fallada. Reprinted by permission of Pantheon Books, New York.

"A Jungle Detective Story" from *Jungle Lore* by Jim Corbett. Reprinted by permission of Oxford University Press, London.

CONTENTS

J. H. Williams   The Presumptuous Tiger 9

Robert M. McClung   Shag: Last of the Plains Buffalo 18

C. Bernard Rutley   Tiger Cub Prisoners 26

Emil E. Liers   Beaver Lodge Visitors 34

Père Castor   Seal Games 41

Grey Owl   The Red Enemy 44

Paul Annixter   The Blasted Pine 50

Charles G. D. Roberts   Stripes, the Unconcerned 68

Mary L. Jobe Akeley   A Man-made Water Hole 80

Raymond Lee Ditmars   A Pair of Kings 87

Svend Fleuron   The Red Ghost 94

Osa Johnson   The Playful Lions 100

Denis Clark   Boomer, a Kangaroo 107

H. Mortimer Batten   Firepoint 120

Jack London   The Battle of the Fangs 131

J. W. Fortescue   The Story of a Red Deer 136

Gerald Durrell   Mostly Monkeys 146

Rudyard Kipling   The Elephants' Dance 152

Jim Kjelgaard   The Lion 162

Gerald Durrell   Shillings from the Fon 175

Olai Aslagsson   Tom, the Grizzly 183

Alden G. Stevens   The Battle with Man 193

Joseph Chipperfield   Grey Shadow, the Wolf 202

Sir Percy Fitzpatrick   Jim's Circus Crocodile 210

Henry Williamson   Tarka's Joyful Water-life 212

W. H. Hudson   Foxes at Play 220

Hans Fallada   Something to Grouse About 224

Jim Corbett   A Jungle Detective Story 232

TO THE READER

A whimsical writer (it was A. A. Milne, to be exact) once wrote at the beginning of a collection of his pieces that if you wanted to read the pieces without taking a minute to read first the words he put in front, it was all right — but it would be like entering a house by climbing through the window; the better way, he suggested, would be to go in comfortably and intelligently, through the door.

If you are one who cannot wait to undo a present, if you have no time to see what message is on the card but must tear off the wrapping and get at the inside, pronto, then skip everything, and when you have enjoyed the stories, come back.

Then you may like to know how these particular stories were brought together. They were chosen among many good ones, picked because they are about natural animals, animals who do not talk in the language of men. These narratives are the work, therefore, of writers who have observed how animals act and how they understand, interpret and communicate in other ways than through words.

The British author, Joseph Chipperfield (whose wolf-dog story, "Grey Shadow", is one of those selected) has explained his point of view — which is that of the present book — saying that when he turned to writing animal stories he "felt strongly that tales in which animals had human thoughts were not animal stories at all. Before I could write about animals, I wanted to know their code of living, their attitudes toward the things they cared about."

The stories are varied in subject; the creatures who pad, stalk, creep, swing, dart, skip, slither, flip, dig, leap, or charge through these pages include lions, leopards, monkeys, kangaroos, skunks, tigers, badgers, bush babies, seals, deer, panthers, king cobras, rhinoceroses, wolverines, wolves, grizzly bears, elephants, giraffes, foxes, antelopes, and gazelles. The stories vary in mood from the dramatic and exciting to the hilarious and farcical, to the touching and inspiriting.

In choosing, the criterion has been for the story to be a good yarn, and one not worn thin with repetition in other books. Freshness and excellence of presentation have been the qualities sought.

Deliberately, one kind of story was set aside, even if it seemed well told. That is the story, thankfully not much written today, which glorifies the hunting and killing of wild animals as an end in itself. In a day when — by way of example — public concern for the dwindling number of birds of a rare species is great enough for the United States Government to issue a special postage stamp to make people aware of these birds, the Florida whooping cranes, how ironic and stupid it would be to single out for attention killers and destroyers of wild life. So the elephant stalker whose only interest is in getting an ivory tusk to be made into tourist curios, the safari leader going out for the personal thrill of destruction, the hunter of tigers whose object is to be photographed with one foot resting on the dead carcass has no place in this collection.

Ernest Thompson Seton expressed the philosophy upon which this book is based when he said at the opening of his *Lives of the Hunted* what he also had said earlier in *Wild Animals I Have Known*: "My chief motive, my most earnest underlying wish, has been to stop the extermination of harmless wild animals — not for their sakes but for ours, firmly believing that each of our native wild creatures is in itself a precious heritage that we have no right to destroy." In similar appreciation of the value of a wild animal breed, the American writer, Emil Liers, warmly and beautifully dedicates

7

his *A Beaver's Story*: "To the beaver: the most diligent of God's creatures, a gentle humorist, a lover of home and family, and America's first colonist, whose sacrifices have helped to make our country great."

It has repeatedly struck the compiler of this collection that the authors of the animal stories, in prefaces to their own books, often mentioned that when they were young, they loved to read what explorers and naturalists and woodsmen had to tell of their exploits and adventures. The mixture of reading and going out into the open to seek and observe made them — the writers who were not yet writers, not yet anything but tadpoles still a-forming — resolve to become explorers and trackers. And they did.

So who shall guess what this book may mean to some one reader? Even though it should prompt no Grey Owl or Gerald Durrell or Paul Annixter or Kipling to take up his career, still if its pages should bring a reader something fine to remember or if they should introduce him to an author whose further acquaintance he will seek, it has been worth the effort. And for it to have conjured pictures out of the paint-pots of that master of the paint brush, Jan Grabianski, has meant pleasure to an ever-widening circle.

To accomplish this has meant great effort on the part of many people but above all Sarah Chokla Gross who has done so much of the hardest and most important work in tracking down stories, facts about their authors and the animals they write about: the thanks of all readers of this book are her due.

Margaret Green

NOTE: Occasional variations in spelling ("center" appearing as "centre", "colour" turning up as "color") mean simply that the stories printed here follow the British or American spelling and punctuation of their original publication.

THE PRESUMPTUOUS TIGER

by J. H. Williams (Elephant Bill)

Elephants play a supremely important part in the life of the Burmese as they are essential to the country's teak trade. It is with these elephants and their riders — oozies — that Col. Williams's life has largely been spent. He has written several books of which the most famous is *Elephant Bill*, the name by which he was known throughout Burma. This story comes from his second book, *Bandoola*, and describes the birth of this elephant which he says was the most interesting and challenging animal with whom he ever had to deal.

Wild elephants consider it the duty of the whole herd to protect an elephant carrying young, but in captivity the "auntie" system prevails. Instinctively they realise that to protect the young calf against the tiger two elephants are needed, and for a whole year before the birth the expectant mother, Ma Shwe, and her auntie, Mee Tway, had grazed together and got to know one another in preparation for the great and dangerous occasion.

The choice of site is a matter for the mother and her "auntie". No tactful suggestions from outsiders are received. Ma Shwe and Mee Tway chose well. They selected a spot where the creek made a crook-shaped bend. That meant they were protected on three sides by water, and it was silently running water. The least sound from the river could be heard. There were plentiful supplies of elephant grass, which meant good fodder. And in the centre was a gigantic Nyaung tree. The Nyaung tree is evergreen. Its roots penetrate so deeply that they sap the underground rivers of the jungle, and the Burmans say that under a scorching sun a Nyaung tree will give off a ton of water a day. The tree provided shade, and two natural buttresses protruding from its base made a bay like a natural stall.

Overnight the mother and the auntie spent a considerable time circling the tree and stamping down the grass until they had flattened an area the size of a circus ring. The maternity ward was complete.

There was little fuss about the birth, though for half an hour there was great tension as Mee Tway went round and round the tree on guard. Then the sun rose and revealed to all the inquisitive eyes of the jungle — squirrels', birds', monkeys' — the tubbiest little male elephant calf ever born.

His trunk was just a deformity of a snout which he could scarcely move; and his small piggy eyes were surrounded with wrinkles, and as deep as those of an elephant over three score years and ten. On his little forehead and along his back were masses of long wavy hair in need of brushing. His toe-nails — five on each fore-foot and four on each hind-foot — looked as if they had just been manicured. His skin fitted snugly over his baby body, but it was serrated and loose at the folds, like baby clothes. His complexion was the kind of purple you get by mixing blue and pink in a paint-box. His little tail touched his hocks and persistent insects were already teaching him its use.

As the sun went down, the clearing seemed to be illuminated with a green eerie light. This was the time when some of the jungle-dwellers were thinking of their sleep and others stretching and licking paws and rubbing sleepy eyes awake. Po Toke, the oozie, knew that the coming night would be the most dangerous of all nights for his calf. As he went down to the creek on his way to camp, he saw that Ma Shwe had walked the fifty yards to the river to drink during his absence and Mee Tway had done likewise at another time. A good mother, a good auntie: they would not leave

the calf unguarded. He was happier than he had ever been. He raised his voice and sang a Burmese love-song as he picked his way from boulder to boulder.

The elephants in their clearing heard his voice, so did a young full-grown tiger in a cane-break four hundred yards away across the stream. The tiger had chosen his lair with the same jungle instinct as the elephants had chosen their maternity ward, but with a different purpose. For days he had crossed and recrossed the track behind Ma Shwe. From the day an elephant's second milk falls into her udders, they leave a strong scent on all the leaves and branches that they touch. This scent had been an instinctive challenge to the tiger. He would kill and eat a baby elephant. It was his first attempt, but he knew that his best chance of doing so was within forty-eight hours of the calf's birth.

Even to approach his prey taxed all his jungle instinct. He knew that soon after sundown the breeze, however light it might be, would shift to downstream as the hot air rose from the valley. So he made his lair below the clearing, ready to work upstream against the breeze after crossing the river.

The tiger's lair was impenetrable. The tendrils of the creeping cane formed a tangled mass around and above it. He entered and left it by a tunnel which was scarcely visible. He had been there for several weeks, and he knew every track and cover-hiding for over a square mile round the camp. As it was the dry season he left no pug-marks in the creeks. He had even starved himself for the last few days, for hunger would increase his courage when the attack came. He knew the calf had been born by the rumbling sounds of pleasure made by the mother. He sat up and washed his face, as Po Toke went singing along the creek. The only sign of his excitement was the twitching of his tail.

Before it was dark the tiger left his lair and crossed the creek a long way below the elephants' pitch. He worked stealthily upstream until his sensitive nostrils picked up the scent of the newborn calf being wafted down on the evening breeze. For some distance he boldly followed the open game-track along the bank of the creek. Then he re-entered the jungle, and for a time squatted motionless on his haunches, working himself up for the attack. There was more in this than hunger and a succulent meal; there was prowess. To attack two elephants and kill the calf would be an achievement worthy of the king of the Burmese jungle.

He could not decide in advance whether he would attack the mother or the auntie first. That would depend on how they were standing when he moved in to attack. But he knew that he could not seize the calf until he had stampeded both the adults. He must spring on the back of one and so lacerate her that she fled for safety; then he must unseat himself and stampede the other long enough to give him time to seize the precious calf and carry it off like a cat with a rat in its mouth.

But before he could attack, he knew that he must circle the clearing, because the best line of attack was from upstream. His patience was superb. Twice he moved up to within fifty yards of the clearing, but each time the breeze was coming downstream too fast for him to risk his scent being carried to them when he moved above.

The moon rose higher and higher, but it was not till well after midnight that the breeze dropped. Utter silence fell on the jungle, a silence so deathly that few human beings can endure it without making some sound or movement to reassure themselves. But the elephants made no sound. The two adults stood side by side, as unmoving as statues in the moonlight; and between the forelegs of his mother, with his little head just filling the gap, stood the baby calf, as motionless as they.

Occasionally the ears of the adult animals moved forward as if straining to hear a sound. Then Mee Tway broke the silence — for no reason — she just thumped the end of her trunk on the ground, and it rang hollowly with a metallic sound.

It eased the tension but it started the tiger on his first circuit round the clearing. He was fifty yards out, and he had decided to make his attack from the creek side. Four times he circled without crackling a leaf or a twig — the perfect hunter. He no longer walked with slow, stealthy step. He was now so near that at any moment he might see his quarry in the clearing. His poise was low on the ground. He moved forward with his powerful hind legs tensed under his body, ready instantly to spring. The tip of his tail quivered.

15

At last he saw the picture he had dreamed of: an elephant's flank clearly silhouetted, and only ten bounds and a leap away. His enormous power was released as he bounded forward and with a seven-foot spring landed on Mee Tway's back. His fore-paws dug deep into the barrel of the elephant's back. The vicious grip of the fore-claws held his weight, while with his hinder claws he lacerated the sides of the wretched elephant. With a murderous snarl he sank his teeth into the elephant's shoulder.

16

For a second Mee Tway was taken by surprise. Then bellowing with panic fear she was off, making for the nearest jungle, where she could shake this savage terror from her back.

As she reached the edge of the untrodden elephant grass she hesitated for a moment; and in that moment the tiger retracted his claws and slid off, as a child might slide from a bareback pony. Immediately he turned and bounded back to attack Ma Shwe, standing under the Nyaung tree with the buttresses of the tree protecting her flanks. She had the advantage of position. The tiger could only attack head on. He had no opportunity to manoeuvre. She was terrified, but she stood her ground, with the calf huddled between her forelegs.

She took one chance. As the tiger checked before her, she took a pace forward and lashed at him with her trunk. With a lightning swing his right paw struck, the very movement of a cat at a terrier's face. The sharp claws struck home and Ma Shwe shrieked and bellowed with pain; for the trunk is the most sensitive and vital organ of the elephant. But she did not stampede. She replaced her off forward foot to protect the calf, who hadn't moved an inch.

But in that moment the tiger had gained his flank position and sprang up on her withers. His fore-claws dug their hold and his hind-claws tore at her flesh. She rolled and shook herself to fling him off, but still she didn't stampede and still he clung and tore.

Her trunk hung limp. She had no means of touching her calf. The injury had made it quite numb and useless. She felt herself weakening. Was there no relief from this murderous weight?

Then suddenly it seemed as if the Nyaung tree had fallen on her. Something struck her with the force of an avalanche. She sank to her knees with the impact, without damaging the calf. And when she rose again, the murderous weight was gone. Mee Tway had returned, goaded to fury by her wounds, and charged at the tiger clinging to the mother's flank.

The king of the Burmese jungle fell to the ground. He was badly hurt in pride and body. But he managed to slide away back to his jungle lair.

Now the two defiant elephants stood side by side once more, the blood streaming from their wounds, but the calf stood perfect and untouched. They raised their heads and roared and trumpeted a challenge to all the tigers of the Ningyan Forest.

17

SHAG: LAST OF THE PLAINS BUFFALO

by Robert M. McClung

Robert M. McClung began being interested in animals when he was a small boy in Pennsylvania. From keeping pets, to studying biology and zoology in college, to seven years on the staff of New York's Bronx Zoo (after active duty in the Navy during World War II), he has progressed toward his present career as a writer and editor of natural-history books. *Shag, Last of the Plains Buffalo,* his seventeenth book about animals, gives a stark picture of the buffalo's struggle to survive the grim winter of 1884.

The days were growing shorter and colder, and all the animals of the plains and hills were making their final preparations for winter. Flocks of honking waterfowl rose in clouds from the rivers and headed south. Beavers were snug in their lodges behind dammed creeks, and muskrats had thick shelters of mud and reeds in the marshes. Deer and elk had left their summer feeding grounds high up in the hills and were wandering down the slopes to the more sheltered lowlands.

One morning in mid-November a heavy bank of dark clouds hung low in the sky and a chill north wind was blowing. By mid-morning snow began to fall. The flakes that whirled around Shag were so thick and hard-driven in the strong wind that he could scarcely see the other animals in the band. Soon a cold white mantle covered his back and blanketed his head. The world was changing very quickly into blinding whiteness and bitter cold.

The buffalo headed into the storm and plodded onward. As hour after hour went by, the blizzard's fury increased. The wind became a ranging gale, driving the frozen snowflakes against Shag like thousands of stinging needles. Sometimes he felt another buffalo jostle his side, but he could not see the other animals at all.

Night fell, bitter and cold, and the storm raged on. By morning Shag was floundering through deep drifts. In some places the wind had already piled the snow into masses many feet thick. And it was still coming down, as cold and heavy and whirling as ever. Some of the buffalo fell over a cliff that afternoon, blinded by the snow. Shag could hear their bellows as they fell to their death on the jagged rocks below.

It wasn't until the third day that the snow stopped falling and the winds died away. At last Shag could see again. All around him was a silent, cold world of sparkling whiteness.

Shag grunted as he plowed through drifts that touched his belly. It was heavy going, for he was hungry and exhausted. Ahead of him an old bull was rooting in the snow. Shag bent his head and nuzzled in the drifts too. Deep down he uncovered a small clump of curled and frozen grass. He seized it eagerly and pulled it loose. After he had chewed and swallowed it, he began to root again. There was food here, but it was going to be hard to get.

Other blizzards raged around the buffalo in the weeks that followed. Snow drifted deeper and deeper in the valleys. This was going to be a harder winter than usual, even for the wild north country. No matter how much Shag rooted, he was never able to uncover enough grass to satisfy his hunger. His sides grew lean, and his ribs were sharp ridges underneath his skin.

Winter was a time of hunger for many animals. Sometimes Shag saw little bands of deer or elk in sheltered areas. They had tramped out paths through the drifts from one cluster of trees or bushes to another. The twigs were eaten up as far the deer could reach.

Hungry wolves ranged far and wide, looking for food. They attacked the deer in their yards and they followed the buffalo, waiting for a chance to kill a snowbound animal or one weakened by starvation. Many of the buffalo died during the cold months.

One afternoon in March Shag wandered into a narrow, rocky canyon. He nudged through the snow, searching, as always, for the few tufts of frozen grass that he might find. Suddenly he glimpsed a tawny shape leaping through the air toward him. The hurtling form knocked him over. He felt razor-sharp talons rip through his thick wool, tearing deep bloody gashes in his sides. A hungry mountain lion had landed on his back.

Bellowing with surprise and pain, Shag plunged and scrambled in the drifts as he tried to regain his footing and dislodge the fierce enemy that was attacking him. The great cat lunged for his throat and its long fangs stabbed into his nose. Frantic with pain, Shag scraped against the canyon wall. The spitting, clawing demon slid off his back at last.

Floundering in the deep snow, Shag turned his head to meet the lion's next charge. He hooked his straight hard horns into the tawny squirming sides, and drove his hoofs into the big cat's soft belly. The mountain lion was having trouble in the deep drifts too.

Yowling with pain, the cat sprang upward, and with one tremendous leap reached a shelf of rock twelve feet away. For a moment it crouched there, snarling. Then it bounded back among the rocks and disappeared.

Shag turned quickly and made his way out of the canyon, back toward the other buffalo. His wounds were not serious, but they were painful. Already the rips on his back and flanks were beginning to stiffen in the freezing air.

A pale sun glimmered in the sky the next day and a mild west wind blew from the mountains. Soon the weather became warmer and the drip, drip, drip of melting snow sounded everywhere. Spring was on its way at last. It was time for the buffalo to start the great trek back to the summer feeding grounds.

The buffalo did not travel all the time. Often they stayed in one place for several days, feeding and resting. As the days went by they met other small bands, coming from every sheltered canyon and winter feeding place. Soon the herd numbered many thousands, a great dark sea of animals surging northward.

In mid-April the buffalo came to a wide, ice-covered river. The leaders hesitated at the bank. Then, pushed forward by the thousands of buffalo behind them, they started across the ice. By the time Shag scrambled onto the frozen surface, the vanguard of the herd was already halfway across. Suddenly he felt the ice swaying beneath him, heard loud cracking noises. Several widening dark lines appeared ahead.

The solid ice broke beneath Shag and the swift, cold water swept over him. Kicking strongly, he rose to the surface, snorting for air. All around him were other struggling buffalo. Many of them were swept under the ice and drowned.

Again and again Shag felt the current pulling him downward, but each time he struggled to the surface. The icy waters chilled him to the bone, and soon he had little strength left to swim any farther. He felt himself being swept under again. His hoofs struck out weakly and touched something solid — the river bottom. He had made it across.

Shag climbed wearily up the bank and followed the other buffalo. Most of the great herd made it to the other side that day, but not all of them. The river had taken its toll.

Day after day the buffalo pressed forward as spring started to cover the land with green. Prairie chickens danced in the morning sunshine, and wild geese honked overhead at night. Calves began to appear among the buffalo — lanky red youngsters that frisked along behind their mothers as Shag had done the year before.

The big herd split up, and the buffalo scattered over the rich grasslands in smaller herds and bands. Shag's ragged sides began to get rounded and fat. He was shedding now, and only shreds and tatters of his thick winter wool still clung to his sides. The new hair was starting to grow in, and his skin was tender and itchy. He used every big tree and rock that he came to as a rubbing post.

Mosquitoes rose in clouds from the marshy low places, almost driving Shag crazy. He spent a lot of his time rolling in muddy wallows, trying to escape the insect tormentors. He hooked his horns into the dirt and sent it flying over his back and sides. He lay down and rolled over and over, scratching his hump, plastering his sides with the soft mud. Then, snorting and blowing, he rose and shook himself. The mud on his sides dried and formed a protective coating against the insects.

Flocks of little brown cowbirds followed the buffalo, eating the insects that swarmed around them. Sometimes three or four of them perched on Shag's back at one time, pecking at the insects in his wool.

Several times that spring and summer Shag saw caravans of the white man's covered wagons heading westward. Each time the white men shot at the buffalo with their dreaded guns.

Spring passed into summer, and week after week the sun blazed down on the plains with no relief. By mid-July, when the bulls began to fight each other for mastery of the herds, the land was dusty and dry from horizon to horizon. As Shag listened to the bellowing of the bulls all around him, he was stirred by a strange excitement.

He was a yearling now — a spike bull. He weighed nearly seven hundred pounds, and had a small but definite hump. His smooth blue-gray horns were six inches long, and he had the beginnings of a beard. He sparred with the other spike bulls, testing his dawning strength. But the adult bulls could send him flying with just a ferocious look, or a shake of their massive heads. Shag still had a lot of growing up to do before he could meet them on even terms.

While the bulls were fighting each other, the plains became drier and dustier than ever. There had been no rain for over three months. By mid-August the creeks and water holes of spring were drying up.

One day a great black cloud came flying out of the east, whirring above the herd with the sound of millions of gauzy wings. It was a vast swarm of locusts. They came to earth in countless numbers, settling on the ground, the bushes, the trees. They covered Shag's back and walked over his eyes. His hoofs crushed locusts with every step.

Millions of tiny champing jaws made a rustling noise all over the land. Soon the locusts had eaten all the grass that was left. Then they ate the leaves of the trees. When there was nothing left to eat they flew away, leaving the land as stripped and bare as a desert.

Day after day the relentless sun beat down. Shag's band wandered far and wide, searching for grass and water. Time and again they came to old water holes, only to find them empty, their cracked bottoms baked hard as pottery.

Late one afternoon the buffalo came to the banks of what had been a river in the spring. Now the river bed lay bare and dry, with only a few shallow stagnant pools in the center. They were enough for the buffalo, though. None of them had tasted water for days.

Frantic with eagerness, the thirst-crazed animals raced over the dried mud. As Shag neared one of the pools he felt the hard mud bottom become softer. The farther he advanced, the deeper his hoofs sank. With each step the muck made sucking noises as he pulled his legs from it.

23

In front of him an old cow was mired in mud almost to her belly. Struggling desperately, she tried to pull herself out of the treacherous sands. But there was no solid footing beneath her hoofs, and the more she struggled the deeper she sank. The grasping quicksand was halfway up her sides. She lowed feebly, her swollen tongue hanging out of her mouth. Soon she was mired so deep that she could not move. A number of other buffalo were caught in the same way.

Shag hesitated for a moment, sensing that something was wrong. But he smelled the water ahead, still out of reach. Pulling with all his strength, he freed one foreleg that had sunk deep into the mud. He took another step forward. Then he pulled the other foreleg free. Step by step he advanced, pulling each leg out of the mud in turn. Ahead of him the footing was firmer. He had missed the worst of the treacherous quicksands.

At last he reached the pool. The water was warm and brown and smelled of decay, but that did not matter. He thrust his nose into it and drank long and eagerly. Other buffalo, pushing and shoving, made their way to the water too. They drank until all the water had disappeared.

For several days Shag and the other survivors wandered along the river bed, searching for more pools. But the fiery sun had reduced most of them to mud. Many of the buffalo became too weak to walk, and lay waiting for death. Shag and the others wandered on. Several times they were fired upon as they approached water holes. Hunters were camped there, waiting to kill any buffalo that came to drink.

Late one afternoon Shag felt the faintest stirring of a cool breeze. He sniffed eagerly as a shadow passed over the sun. Gray clouds were rolling over the distant mountaintops. Soon they were directly overhead. He felt a drop of rain hit his back. Several big drops spattered near him, each hitting the parched earth with a plopping sound, each sending up a tiny spurt of dust as it hit. In a few minutes rain came pouring down, a hard, drenching storm that sent water across the steaming plains in tiny rivulets, filling every depression and buffalo wallow with water.

Shag and the other buffalo drank as if they would never get enough. They rolled in the filling wallows and let their dried skins soak up the moisture. Drought and storm and snow might kill many buffalo, but some would survive. It had always been that way.

TIGER CUB PRISONERS

by C. Bernard Rutley

C. Bernard Rutley has written many nature books, some in conjunction with his wife. In this story from *Wild Life in the Jungle* he shows what excellent mothers tigers are and how they will face their most dreadful fears in defence of their young.

In those early days Timur and Ranee were just two little helpless kittens, with large ears, and paws big out of all proportion to their size, and every day, when Mother Sita carried them into the sunshine, they staggered aimlessly around just as small domesticated kittens do. But those feeble staggerings were developing baby muscles. Daily Timur and Ranee grew stronger, and in the evenings, after she had fed them and seen them safely asleep inside the cave, Sita and her lord went hunting. They went different ways, and one night Khan would make a kill and the next night Sita would be successful, and always the fortunate one, having eaten, called the other to partake of the feast.

Meanwhile Timur and Ranee were growing apace. The aimless staggerings gave place to kittenish play. They chased each other. They wrestled and fought mimic battles, or else played hide-and-seek round Mother Sita's great striped body as she lay stretched contentedly in the sunshine. Sometimes, greatly daring, they would even play with Father Khan, making half-hearted attempts to pounce on his tail. But they did this only when he was well-fed and in a good temper, and always they were very careful not to vex him. For the first thing Sita had taught Timur and Ranee was to respect their father.

Now, usually the tiger-folk and the inhabitants of Indian villages respect each other's rights. So long as a tiger is not a man-eater, and does not take undue toll of their goats and cattle, the Indian villagers will leave him in peace. But it happened that in the village near which Khan and his family lived there was a man named Saji Rao who was avaricious. Saji Rao, in fact, loved money; therefore when one day a fellow-villager brought news of the tiger family living in the forest a mile away and of the two fine young cubs, Saji Rao pricked up his ears.

Tiger cubs sold in the right quarter meant money, and he knew a man who bought wild animals for foreign zoos. So Saji Rao prepared his plans. He had a son and a nephew to help him, and so well were their plans laid that three evenings later they found the cave in the gully unguarded, popped the protesting cubs into stout sacks, and regained the village without accident. Thereupon they tied the cubs up in a corner of the hut, and fell asleep to dream of the good rupees in store for them.

Now began two days of terror for Timur and Ranee. Saji's son, into whose care the cubs were given while his father went off to find a purchaser, fed them and treated them kindly, but the man-scent scared them, and they missed Mother Sita, so that they whined and spat whenever the boy went near them. As for Sita, she was a mad thing. Returning home in the early morning, full and contented after a good night's hunting, her first warning of something amiss was the dreaded man-scent near the cave. Instantly she halted and growled, her tail swishing angrily to and fro as she glared to right and left into the bushes. But nothing stirred — even the monkey-folk, who knew what had taken place, were for once silent, dreading what might happen next. A moment later, made anxious by the absence of the hungry cries which usually greeted her home-coming, the tigress dashed into the cave and found it empty.

29

Then followed a time of fear for all the forest-folk. Roaring her anguish, Sita rushed hither and thither searching for her cubs, until presently, remembering the man-scent, she returned to the cave and followed the trail to the edge of the clearing in which the village stood. But beyond that she dared not go. On all sides the men-folk were working in their fields, so, after glaring at them with blazing eyes, and roaring her rage and sorrow, Sita flashed about and rushed back into the forest.

All that day the tigress ranged to and fro, while over the forest lay an unearthly silence. Many of the wild-folk fled from the neighbourhood, while those who remained crouched shivering in their lairs. For once the monkeys forgot to chatter, the peafowls to screech and scream. Even Khan kept out of his mate's way, while Thunda the Buffalo, who feared nothing, turned aside to give the raging tigress free passage. For in her misery, Sita's one thought was to kill, kill, kill, and none of the forest-folk, however brave, cared to face a mother tigress robbed of her cubs.

Evening came, and Sita returned to the clearing. Instinct told her that her cubs were in the village, and standing in the gloom of the forest, she roared forth her challenge until the shivering villagers lit great fires to keep her at bay. What a night that was! Up and down at the edge of the clearing stalked Sita, tireless in her hate and fury. At intervals she stopped to send her roar crashing through the darkness, while the terrified villagers piled fuel and still more fuel upon their fires, and in their prison Timur and Ranee whimpered and growled until, in desperation, Saji's son muzzled them to keep them quiet.

Poor Timur, poor Ranee! They could hear their mother, but could not reach her, and when morning came, and Sita's voice ceased to call from the forest, they must have thought themselves deserted. At least, so concluded Saji's son.

"All will be right now," he said to his mother as he fed the cubs on warm milk. "The tigress has forgotten them, and when father returns we shall sell them for much money."

So also thought the other villagers, for with the coming of daylight Sita had slunk away into the forest. But Sita had not forgotten her cubs, she had only changed her tactics. It was no good roaring at the men-creatures. Roaring didn't make them release Timur and Ranee, it only made them bring forth those terrible fire-things which even Sita's courage feared to face, so she determined to see what silence would do. All day she lay in a dense thicket, not troubling to hunt, though she was ravenously hungry, and only going once to the stream to drink, and when darkness came again she returned to the clearing. But this time she went silently, and lying down in the shadows, she watched the village with great smouldering eyes.

Meanwhile the villagers had recovered from the previous night's scare. The tigress had forgotten her cubs. All was well. So they went to sleep unconscious of the great striped creature which crouched at the edge of the forest, and which presently began to creep towards the village as silently as a shadow. Yard by yard Sita advanced. Half-way across the clearing she stopped and glared into the darkness. In the village a pariah yelped, then another. Sita's lips curled in a snarl and her great head moved from side to side. There were none of the fire-things she dreaded. The men-creatures had gone into their caves. The tigress resumed her stealthy advance. Soon she was close to the first hut, and sniffed gustily, hoping to pick up the scent of her babies; at the same instant a wandering pariah caught sight of the long shadowy form, uttered a yelp of terror, and fled screaming through the night.

Immediately the village was awake. At the scream of the pariah every dog within hearing began to bark, while from inside the huts came the chatter of voices raised in alarm. What was happening? Sita crouched flat on the ground, growling, her tail swishing angrily to and fro and her eyes glancing anxiously this way and that. The sound of the human voices scared her, but stronger than her fear was her longing for her cubs. Where were they? Sita's eyes smouldered fiercely. The next moment a frightened whimpering reached her from a nearby hut, and at the sounds all doubts vanished and with a deep-throated roar the tigress sprang forward.

Now pandemonium broke out. Hearing their mother's voice, Timur and Ranee redoubled their cries, and a second later there came a terrific crash as the furious tigress hurled herself against the door of the hut. Instantly the shrieks of frightened women were added to the uproar, while Sita, half-famished with hunger, crazed with longing for her cubs, and scared by the noise, lost all control of herself. Madly she flung her body against the sides of the hut. She tore at it with her mighty claws, she tried to wrench it apart with her teeth, till the flimsy structure shook and creaked and appeared as though it must collapse at any moment before the fury of her onslaught.

Meanwhile inside the hut of Saji Rao terror reigned.

"Where is your father's gun?" screamed Saji Rao's wife, addressing her son.

"It is here, my mother," answered the boy, "but there are no cartridges."

"Throw the cubs out of the window," cried the boy's grandmother. "It is the cubs the tigress wants. Throw them out, you fool, and she will go away!"

"Yes, throw them out!" screamed Saji Rao's two daughters. And, "Throw the cubs to the tigress. Give the cubs back to their mother," echoed different voices from neighbouring huts in various tones of alarm.

"But my father! What will my father say?" screamed Saji Rao's son.

"Your father, fool! What does it matter what your father says, when at any moment the demon outside may burst in and kill us?" yelped the boy's mother. "If you will not throw them out, I will," and, pouncing upon the cubs, the woman threw them one after the other out of the narrow opening which served as a window.

Instantly the attack ceased. As Timur's small body thudded to the ground, Sita picked him up in her mouth and bounded away into the darkness. For a few seconds she was gone; then she was back again for Ranee, and thus in turn she carried them across the clearing and into the forest. There she suckled them, feeding the poor, frightened, little cubs on warm, comforting milk, and when at last the whimperings changed to baby purrs of gratification, she picked them up in her mouth and continued the journey home.

BEAVER LODGE VISITORS

by *Emil E. Liers*

The little Iowa town on the Mississippi where Emil L. Liers spent his boyhood gave him plenty of opportunity for the occupations he liked best: fishing and trapping. At twenty-two, he and his wife moved into a houseboat and floated with the Mississippi until their little girl was of school age.

The day came when trapping held no more appeal for Liers, and he began instead to collect wild creatures alive. He established in Minnesota the world's only otter sanctuary, and there, watching several generations of these animal comedians, he was prompted to write his first book, *An Otter's Story*.

In his next book, *A Beaver's Story*, at one point a flood brings unexpected company into the snug underground lodge of the beavers, Akella, Haloka, and their kits. Not all the visitors are friends; some would gladly eat certain others. The beavers keep aloof. Emil Liers evokes the warm feeling of family unity among the beavers, especially in what happens after the intruders have left.

From late November to early March the slough was covered with a sheet of ice. Snug and warm in their well-built lodge, the beavers were hardly aware of the snow and bitter cold outside. Akella and Haloka drowsed long hours away, enjoying a well-deserved rest from their summer and fall of steady work. In the various underground rooms and runways the kits played tag and hide-and-seek, sometimes even venturing up into the trunk of the hollow elm overhead.

When the family was hungry Akella or Haloka would dive out into the chilly water under the ice to bring in a branch for supper. Often they could not pull out a limb intact, for it might be six inches thick and held tight in the mesh of other branches. Then they would close their lips tightly behind their incisors and cut the limb off neatly, with no danger of choking or inhaling any water. Without extensive woodcutting to keep their teeth worn down, the beavers' incisors tended to grow too long in winter. To remedy this, they often cut the peeled sticks that were left over after dinner into shorter and shorter lengths, ending up with cone-shaped pieces of wood and a bed of fresh shavings; or shredded them into slivers, as a tooth-shortening exercise.

As the end of winter approached, the kits grew restless. They longed for spring and the freedom to roam in the pool and along the banks of the slough. Early in March a spell of warm weather and thaw brought them an unexpected diversion. The thaw had caused the river and sloughs to rise, and thirteen muskrats were flooded out of their den in a nearby inlet. In looking for a new burrow under the ice, they happened upon one of the beavers' auxiliary runways.

Akella and Haloka were a bit suspicious of the newcomers at first, but they allowed them to make a nest at one side of the runway. The kits were very curious about these little creatures. The adult muskrats were not more than half the size of the beaver kits, and their feeble, ratlike tails seemed pitiful to the beavers, so proud of their own broad paddles. But each family left the other to its own devices, and there was no trouble between the neighbors.

A few days later another caller arrived who was not nearly so welcome. A large male mink swam into the muskrats' runway, looking for food. A muskrat dinner would have suited him fine, but all thirteen swam off in alarm the moment he appeared. The mink was too wise to bother the beavers in their inner lodge. He decided to wait in the runway for the muskrats' return. But the muskrats were not so foolish. While the hungry mink lay dozing and waiting for them, they had traveled under the ice to the old fallen maple where the beaver kits had once nested. There the muskrats made themselves at home, and even found some clams for breakfast.

The mink was still drowsing in the runway when he felt an upsurge of waves slapping at the entrance. Expecting to catch a returning muskrat, he crouched for the kill. To his great surprise there appeared in the entrance not a muskrat but the head of a big, sleek otter. In great alarm the mink turned and dashed up the runway. He whisked into the beavers' quarters without so much as a by-your-leave, and before the startled beaver family could collect their wits he sprang up through the opening into the hollow elm tree and was gone.

Akella and Haloka were just exchanging indignant grunts when a big otter also bounded into their living room. This was the big male who had startled the mink, and after him came his mate and three boisterous young otter cubs! With great good nature the otters ambled up to Akella and Haloka, sniffing inquisitively and chuckling their otter small talk. The otter cubs scampered about, trying to coax the astonished beaver kits into a game. But the beaver family was not amused. Their peaceful, sober natures resented this intrusion into their home, and they could not understand these happy-go-lucky trespassers.

Akella and Haloka humped their backs and hissed warningly at the interlopers. The mother otter saw that they were not wanted in the beaver lodge, and, chuckling to her mate and cubs, she led the merry crew back the way they had come, out under the ice, and on about their carefree wandering. Akella and Haloka soon regained their composure, content to have their placid life restored. But the beaver kits, especially Ossi, felt a faint, persistent longing for another chance to meet those playful otter youngsters.

Toward the end of March the ice began to rot along the course of the beavers' underwater routes around the feed pile. Each time before they dived out into the water, the beavers took deep breaths. As they swam, the breath they gradually exhaled rose in large bubbles through the water and clung to the under surface of the ice. The beavers' fur also released small bubbles as they swam, and gradually their habitual pathways were marked by a ribbon of these

bubbles. When the warm weather came, these ribbons were the first part of the ice cover to break and melt.

On a day in early April, Akella broke through the ice for the first time since December. He called excitedly to Haloka and the kits, and soon they were all sitting side by side on the edge of the ice, combing and cleaning their fur. The mild, fresh air smelled and felt like nectar after their long winter in the lodge. Akella waddled across the honeycombed ice and felled a cottonwood on the bank. He dragged the whole tree back with him to the air hole, and the family feasted on the fresh bark. It tasted delicious after their monotonous diet from the feed pile, for the bark of the stale, stored branches was now beginning to sour. When they had eaten all they could, Haloka cut up the remaining branches and each beaver carried a branch back under the ice and into the lodge for future snacks.

The ice went quickly when the warm south winds began to blow. Soon the water in the slough was free, the pintails and widgeons were flying north, and the great blue herons returned from the south to feed in the ponds and marshes. In a hollow basswood on the bluff the great horned owl's babies were already half grown. The hooded mergansers were hunting for hollow trees to nest in, and all of nature seemed to be expecting new life.

Even Haloka was acting in a strange new manner. She bustled about, cleaning the lodge chambers and runways with great thoroughness, and she insisted that Akella and the kits dig several new dens

in the banks nearby. She herself spent a long time enlarging one of the sleeping rooms in the lodge and shredding a large pile of soft wood shavings to line its floor.

The kits did not quite understand what all these new housekeeping arrangements were about, but they were too full of spring to care. They reveled in swimming up and down the slough, exploring every bay and inlet, every crawfish chimney and muskrat burrow. They cut fresh cottonwood or swamp-ash saplings whenever they were hungry. The old, soured wood left over from the winter feed pile they cut into appropriate lengths and added to the reinforcements around the lodge and runways.

The kits were half as big as their parents now, one year old and growing more independent every day. Yukpa was catching up to her sister Minido in size and strength, and the two of them were nearly a match for their brothers in a tug-of-war contest or an underwater race. Ossi still tagged along close to his idol Akella whenever he was allowed to. Building was what he loved to do most of all; none of the other kits was quite as skillful at it as he. Ossi could cut a tree so fast that the chips flew, and he always seemed to know how to make it fall so that its top would not lodge in the other treetops.

Weki had learned a lot too during the previous year. He was not nearly as clumsy as he had been as a baby, and as he grew older he had learned to control his temper. He hadn't outgrown his appetite, though, and Ossi and Yukpa still teased him now and then. But Weki no longer minded their pestering so much and went calmly about his business. Minido stuck up for him whenever a real quarrel seemed to be brewing, and her good-tempered influence helped to keep everyone happy.

One morning in May, after a long, busy night helping Akella prepare the new dens in the slough bank, the kits swam into the lodge, ready for bed. They had not seen their mother all that night, but they assumed she was still busy with housecleaning in the lodge. What was the kits' surprise and delight to find Haloka curled up in the fresh nest in the burrow, surrounded by five brand-new beaver babies! There were three little brothers and two little sisters for the yearling kits to play with in the months to come. Haloka showed off the new arrivals to their big sisters and brothers, tenderly nuzzling all nine of their children and watching fondly as they nudged and sniffed one another.

The yearlings wanted to take the babies out to play at once, but Haloka let them know that the babies had already had more than enough excitement for their first twenty-four hours. Akella called to the yearlings from outside the lodge. They tumbled out excitedly, eager to tell him the wonderful news. But wise Akella already seemed to know all about the new kits. He swam about as gaily as the yearlings, happy and proud of his fine big family. At last he led the kits into the new bank den that had been prepared and helped them settle down for the day. This would be the yearlings' sleeping place for the rest of the summer, for the new kits needed quiet and Haloka's undivided attention, just as the yearlings had when they were babies.

SEAL GAMES

by Père Castor

This description of seal children at play comes from *Scaf the Seal* which is one of a series of stories of wild animals told by Père Castor. He is French. Dag is Scaf's great grandfather who leads his family through all kinds of exciting and dangerous adventures until Scaf is grown up and able to succeed him.

It was past the middle of winter; the Arctic night was drawing to a close. The sun had begun to put in a timid appearance in the sky. The ice-floe, flat as a table, stretched away to infinity under a blanket of powdery snow. Its edges stood out, clearly defined against an open arm of the sea, in rosy headlands and blue bays, like those of an island. Shoals of cod and caplin moved about in crowds.

Dag and his people lived comfortably by fishing, and grew visibly fatter.

The youngsters gambolled gaily about in the snow and had great games in the water.

It was Scaf who led the games.

The parties of "Herring-ball" were very popular. Pesca would fling a herring into the air with his head and the others had to catch it before it dropped.

"Leap-seal" was also one of their games. One of the players would swim on the surface of the water and another would vault over him and then make off as fast as he could go. The first would then rush after him and leap over him in turn.

"Fish-pouncing" was another favourite amusement. Slim, Kara, Negli and the rest would decide upon one particular fish that could be seen moving about a little below the surface. Then, having taken up their positions, they would all make a dash for their prey at the same moment. It was usually Scaf who came off victorious in these submarine matches.

Pesca's speciality was the pretty game of "Feather-dive". He would watch the sea-swallows flying above the water, and when he saw one of them fold its silvery wings preparatory to pouncing upon a wretched hake, Pesca would dash down at lightning speed, snap up the fish and cheat the bird of its meal.

Scaf broke the seals' official immersion record (which is twenty minutes) by forty and two-thirds seconds. At the end of it his neat little muzzle appeared again on the surface. His nostrils, which while under water were hermetically sealed, were wide open in order to take in a big breath of air. There was hardly time to distinguish his wavy moustache and beautiful eyes before he disappeared again.

Scaf and his friends often went on excursions under the ice. When they wanted to breathe they would break the ice by hitting it with their heads — bang, bang! Then, scratch, scratch, they would make a hole with their flappers. That was how they pierced the ice-floe so that the young ones, the baby brothers, the tiny one-year-olds, could get under the ice without fear of being drowned.

The young folk didn't stay in one place. With their eyes open and their nostrils closed they would be off shrimp-hunting among the green seaweed in the recesses of the deep, or would tear the sea-urchins from the crevices of submerged rocks. They plundered the sand-banks at the bottom of the sea of shell-fish and star-fish. They set off on voyages of discovery in search of the strange landscapes and mysterious inhabitants of the world of waters, and when they returned from these distant expeditions they always caused a great commotion among the glittering ice-fields.

But alas! suddenly ill-fortune befell them. About the middle of April a company of sharks arrived from none knew where and sowed

death and disaster among the seals. Twelve of Dag's great-grand-nephews were destroyed by the teeth of these terrible monsters. Five more were killed by the cruel weapon of the sword-fish. An expedition under the leadership of Slim fell into a walrus ambush; nine of his comrades perished under the attack of these fierce monsters.

This put an end to all their happy excursions. Scaf, Slim and Kara had but one thought — that of avenging the death of their relatives. The mother seals were all anxious to leave these deadly waters. Old Dag was still in doubt as to what course to take, when the cold quite suddenly redoubled in intensity. In a few days the arm of the sea which was still open water became frozen over as far as the island. The seals now found that they were prisoners beneath the ice-floe. They cleared the air-chimneys that were choked with snow; some of them they enlarged, and made hollows in the ice above the water-level where they could take shelter from the attacks of the monsters of the deep.

A few white bears put in an appearance, prowled about the rocks, and then continued their never-ending pilgrimage across the ice deserts.

The seals kept a constant look-out. They always climbed on to the ice-floe with great caution, ready to disappear on the slightest alarm.

THE RED ENEMY

by *Grey Owl*

Grey Owl who wrote this, claimed to be a Canadian Indian called in his own language Wa-Sha-Quon-Asin. He became a hunter as was the tradition of his people but later he grew to be passionately interested in the preservation of wild life and especially beavers. He wrote several wonderful books about these creatures. *Sajo and Her Beaver People* from which this comes is the story of an Indian boy, Shapian, and his sister, Sajo, and their two pet beavers Chilawee and Chikanee, Big Small and Little Small. At the time of this episode Chikanee has had to be sold to a zoo but Chilawee is so miserable alone that the children are determined to find him and buy him back. They set off in their canoe with Chilawee and after many days comes one of the climaxes of their Great Adventure.

One morning they awoke to find a faint smell of wood-smoke in the air, a smell of burning moss and scorching brush and leaves, and they knew that somewhere, seemingly far away, there was a forest fire. But it was closer than they had at first supposed, for as soon as they were well out on the lake and were able to look about them, they could see an immense pillar of smoke billowing up from behind the distant hills; and they did not paddle very far before they found that their route would bring them more and more in its direction. The lake was getting very narrow, and farther on it ended and became a river, across which the fire could easily jump, and Shapian determined to get through this narrow place as quickly as possible, to a large lake that lay beyond, where they would be safe. So they hurried on, and as they went the smoke spread higher and wider, so that it was no longer a pillar, but a white wall that seemed to reach the sky, and rolled outwards and down in all directions, becoming thicker and thicker until the sun was hidden, and the air became heavy and stifling, and very still. The whole country to the eastward seemed to be on fire, and although the blaze itself was hidden by the hills, even at that distance there could be heard a low moaning sound that never ceased and was, minute by minute, becoming closer, and heading straight towards them — they were right in the path of the fire. The big lake was some distance away, across a portage, and there was no time to be lost if they were to cross over to it before the fire rushed down upon them; for, while some forest fires move slowly, others have been known to travel as fast as thirty miles an hour.

44

As the hot smoke cooled off, it began to come down, settling in a dark, blue haze over all the land, making far-off points invisible and near ones look dim, so that soon nothing could be seen but the row of trees nearest the shore-line, and the children were only able to keep their right direction by watching this, and by the sound of the rapids that lay ahead of them.

And above the thunderous roar of the tumbling waters there came the duller, deeper, and terribly frightening sound of the oncoming fire. Smoke poured across the river in dense, whirling clouds and through it sped the leaping canoe with its crew of three. Shapian strained and fought with his paddle and all of his young strength, against the mighty power of the racing torrent. Once he looked back, to find that the fire had crossed the narrow lake behind them; now there was only one way to go — forward, though he said never a word to Sajo about it. The air, that had been thick with heavy rolls and banks of smoke, now commenced to turn darker and darker, and the light was dimmed till it appeared almost

as though twilight had fallen, so early in the day, and hardly anything could be seen around them; and nothing seemed real any more, and they moved like people in a dream.

Desperately Shapian drove the canoe ahead, for well he knew that if they were caught in this place they would be either burnt alive or suffocated. By now the portage was not very far, and beyond it lay the lake that they must get to — and get to fast!

They shot out from the foot of the rapids into a deep, still pool, and here they found themselves surrounded by strange moving shapes, dimly seen through the smoke-clouds, as on all sides all manner of animals were passing, tearing along the shore, or swimming through the pool, or splashing noisily along the shallows, by ones and twos, separately or in small groups, all headed for the big lake, the same one our own travellers were aiming for, each and every one making for the safety that he knew he would find there. Animals that seldom wetted their feet were swimming in the pool — squirrels, rabbits, woodchucks, and even porcupines. Deer leaped through or over the underbrush, their white tails flashing, eyes wide with terror. A bear lumbered by at a swift, clumsy gallop, and a pair of wolves ran, easily and gracefully, beside a deer — their natural prey; but they never even looked at him. For none were enemies now; no one was hungry, or fierce, or afraid of another. And all the people of the woods, those that went on two legs and others that had four, and those with wings and some that swam, animals and birds and creeping things, creatures, some of them, that dared not meet at any other time, were now fleeing, side by side, from that most merciless of all their foes, dangerous and deadly alike to every one of them from the smallest to the greatest — The Red Enemy of the Wilderness, a forest fire.

Right before the canoe, deep in the water, stood a giant bull moose, largest of all the forest folk, his hair scorched from his back, one of his half-grown horns gone, his sides heaving as he sucked in great, deep breaths of air; he must have been nearly caught, and perhaps had run many miles with the fire close behind him, and had only escaped because of his enormous strength and speed. Shapian could have touched him with his paddle had he wished, but the huge beast paid them no attention, and getting his wind again, plunged ashore and joined the other creatures of all shapes and sizes that, all brothers now in this great calamity, were hurrying together to the safety of the lake.

49

THE BLASTED PINE

by *Paul Annixter*

Paul Annixter's stories of outdoor life, of animals and man, have their basis in experience. The author, like the late Denis Clark, found school considerably less attractive than hunting and trapping or taking the high road to Somewhere Else. At eighteen, he left school in Minneapolis and went adventuring, on foot, on the rails, according to what offered.

Eventually, he took up a timber claim in Minnesota. If it was a fiasco as far as making a fortune in timber was concerned, the hard times he endured gave Annixter plenty of material to use later in stories of wolves, panthers, deer, and other wild creatures — among them the carcajou.

Annixter's stories, more than 400 of them since the first one was published in 1926, have appeared in sports-and-outdoors magazines in the United States, Canada, and Great Britain. They have been gathered into several books, including *The Devil of the Woods*, from which is taken the following dramatic tale of that wily, despicable low-life, the wolverine or carcajou.

November had laid its melancholy hush over the far northern valley of the Kinnebec. The bare-branched hardwoods along the slopes made delicate tracery against the marble skies, and the winds coursing down from the rocky ramparts at the valley's head whispered eerily of imminent snow.

Toward the end of a gloomy afternoon a curious-looking animal might have been seen making his way down the valley, coming from the heavy spruce forests to the north. The newcomer was a giant wolverine, a creature who seems predestined for evil, whose fangs and claws are against every other dweller of the wilderness. The various other names he went by — Injun devil, carcajou, glutton and bad dog — were each an epithet coming from a different tongue, expressing ultimate loathing. Ishmael would have been another, equally appropriate, for his arrant genius for deviltry and destruction has made this little beast the most thoroughly hated creature that prowls.

Though it was broad daylight, the newcomer progressed with a total unconcern, keeping to the open places as nothing but the lordly moose and the black bear ever venture to do. His movement was a curious double shuffle, a swagger full of truculent assurance, though as to size he was under three feet in length. But wise as he was beyond all the other creatures of the wild, and of a savage ferocity which few would dare to cross even if his musky flesh were appetizing, which it was not, he had good reason to loaf before the mightiest he knew.

Ishmael was the largest and fiercest member of the *Mustelidae* family, which includes the weasels, minks, martens, and all the professional assassins of the wilderness world. Ishmael inherited the worst elements of all his unsavory ancestors, and the fine qualities of none, unless one counted his courage. He had courage, as all things must which live outside the law. For the rest, he was surlier than a badger, more odious than any skunk, and more ferocious even, for his size, than the fisher marten, his first cousin. A fox was stupid beside him, and he possessed a strength greater for his weight than any other living beast.

Some perversion of his hybrid nature inspires this little beast wantonly to rob, destroy and make trouble with fiendish ingenuity in all his encounters with other creatures, yet there is no experienced trapper but will admit that he is the most wily and efficient of all the forest marauders.

Ishmael was at present in search of a new hunting range, nor had he any scruple as to poaching upon the preserves of others. In all such matters he was a law unto himself. The gloomy valley of the Kinnebec, with its dark ravines mantled with spruce, appealed to him. Here the dense, century-old growth of evergreens excluded

all sunlight; the tangled windfalls of a valley bottom made a laby-
rinth of lairs, run-ways and ambushes. Through the perpetual
twilight beneath the spruce he moved like a spirit of the place, his
black ominous head low hung and swinging. Ishmael's gait more
than anything else epitomized the malign nature of him. He lurched
like a swagman on his short thick legs, and his back kept arching
with the sinister undulations of a measuring worm.

That night the carcajou slept in a hole in the top of an ancient
stump. He did not take the trouble to keep an ear cocked for danger,
for his evil reputation made even the cougar and the wolf, his most
dangerous enemies, think long before disputing ground with him.
Having thus formally taken over the district, his inordinate appetite
had him stirring in the cold black hour before the dawn to exact a
tribute. By nature he was a night prowler, but his long migration had
thrown him temporarily out of his nocturnal bent. Up along the
spruce-grown slope of the valley he drifted as the gray began to

waver in the east. His soundless penetration of the tangled thickets was a marvel and a diablerie for so squat and logy a form, but his entire resource lay in this amazing craft and stealth.

Presently in the black shadows of a juniper thicket he almost stepped on something warm that stirred. A beast of any other persuasion would have leaped back in a momentary start, but the wolverine had not even an instant's recoil. With no perceptible pause his fangs buried themselves in the throat of the tiny spotted fawn that lay there. Though his nose was second to no living thing's in keenness, it had given him no warning, for in the first few weeks of life the fawn has no scent.

Only one broken bleat of terror marked the slaying as Ishmael's powerful jaws met in the baby's neck. Crouched above his prey, Ishmael remained for a moment moveless. If the mother deer happened to be near, her infuriated rush might prove dangerous even to him, but in this instance the doe had wandered far.

Ishmael drank deep of the warm blood, after which he settled down like the trencherman he was, to the process of packing as much solid meat into his system as it could hold without bursting. The mere slaking of his hunger pangs was negligible in this beast's hunting; he lived for gluttony, prolonged orgies of gorging and the deep feeding dreams which followed.

As he was licking his black lips with omnivorous satisfaction over the repast, a stirring in the nearby thicket froze him to the fixity of stone. He glared in the direction of the sound, but instead of the vengeful mother of the fawn, a great black head emerged from the undergrowth, swaying cumbrously from side to side as its owner tested the breeze. It was a full-grown she-bear of an extraordinary size, and the sight of her brought the carcajou's lips twitching up from his teeth. This particular she-bear was his specific and deadly enemy, and he had thought her many miles away to the north. She had reason to remember him as well. Only two months before he had dispatched her single cub, whom he found playing alone in a sunny glade, afterward narrowly escaping the old mother's wrath.

The smell of the fresh blood reached the bear's keen nose. With the time for hibernating close at hand she was in great need of rich, strong feeding to sustain her through the winter months. She came straight on, and for a moment the rage of the carcajou was so great that it almost seemed to efface the disparity of their statures. Then he did that which more than anything else illustrated his diabolic nature: he befouled the carcass of the fawn with the vile-smelling musk from his scent bag.

The nose of the bear brought back the old association and she flung herself savagely forward. But ten feet ahead of her the wolverine turned and slipped like a shadow into the undergrowth. His enemy fell upon the kill and tore a piece from the carcass to set her brand of possession upon it. But that mouthful was never swallowed. Though the fawn's meat would have been a godsend to the bear at this time, the overpowering reek of carcajou nauseated her. No other living thing could eat of that meat now, and the carcajou knew it well. To have the meat snatched from her in so vile and indirect a manner loosed a raging demon in the old bear. She pivoted about on her hind quarters and flung away on the wolverine's trail.

But the few moments gained had been ample time for Ishmael's wily brain to light on a clever ruse. Two hundred feet away he

came upon an ancient blowdown, uprooted by a long-ago storm, its dead bulk leaning against one of its living neighbors. Part of its shattered top overhung a rocky ravine which dropped thirty feet to the tops of the evergreens below. Up the leaning bole Ishmael clambered, and near the top splatted himself flat to wait. In two minutes the she-bear emerged from the thicket hot on his trail and, sighting the despoiler in the topmost crotch, instantly started climbing. The dead conifer trembled under her weight; the carcajou dug his claws into the trunk and bared his teeth in soundless menace. He knew what he must do now and he was ready, but still in no hurry. The farther the bear mounted the trunk the better. Finally when she was but a few feet below him, he steadied himself, then launched downward into space.

It was a desperate feat, yet he had done it many times before in a similar predicament. Claws widespread he crashed sprawling into the tops of the spruce below, and as he struck, his powerful forelegs clutched the branches with all his strength. The tough resilient limbs bent almost double as he slithered down among them, but they did not break. He dropped the last fifteen feet to the ground amidst a shower of broken twigs, unhurt except for a cut in his hide beneath the right foreleg.

On the ground he crouched motionless, listening, until silence pervaded the forest once more. He had hoped the bear might hurl herself after him and dash herself to pieces, but mad as she was she was not rash enough for that. He was safe for the time.

Through the confusion of the windfalls he picked a twisty course with a cunning he knew would put the bear to the limit of her skill to follow; then he sought a cleft in the rocks to rest and lick his bruises. The appearance of his enemy somewhat blighted the outlook on his new range, but he knew that soon she would be forced to hole up and leave him a free agent for the winter months.

Next day the first of the November snows came sifting through the pines. It was dusk on this day when the wolverine caught his first glimpse of his other and more dangerous enemies of the valley, of whose existence he had not dreamed. Searching for a winter den, he saw two men upon the slope above him. Noiseless as a shadow the carcajou slipped after them, drawn by an equal fear and fascination, intent on studying the men and marking the place where they dwelt. Hate was written on his black face and in his glowering eyes. Craftily he dogged their footsteps, unknown and unseen. Once the woodsmen both stopped and stood motionless, peering back with an intuitive sense of being followed. But the carcajou stopped at the same instant, masking himself in the thickets.

To the very edge of the woodsmen's clearing he followed, led by his malign curiosity. There he flattened himself beneath a low balsam and watched until the men had closed their door for the night. He circled the cabin then, familiarizing himself with the scent of his enemies, imprinting upon his consciousness all the details of the clearing. To his way of thinking, these two men were simply interlopers upon a promising range which belonged rightly to him, and then and there he set himself to devising means by which their life here would be made intolerable.

The Wyant brothers, Eben and Jude, had built their splitlog cabin at the head of the Kinnebec Valley. Ostensibly the brothers were backwoods farmers; they had cleared a meager two acres, fought the stumps and stones, and each year planted corn and potatoes. But all this was mere summer makeshift for the Wyants. These lank woodsmen were true sons of the wilderness; life for them didn't really begin till fall set in and they took up the activities of the trap line and the hunting trail.

It was on the morning after the wolverine had followed them home that the brothers began laying several trapping lines for the winter months. The lines ran along the densely wooded valley bottom and up the larger ravines. The utmost craft was used in their setting. Among the tangled blowdowns they devised clever snares and deadfalls of logs which often proved more efficient than the best of traps. The light fall of snow which had begun the day before continued and worked into their hands that day, obliterating all tracks. But it worked into the hands of the small slouching form that followed them as well.

For all unknown to them Ishmael had that morning taken up his agreeable game of shadowing again. He had seen the brothers leave their cabin and had followed at a discreet distance to see what they were about. Eyes bright with malign sagacity, Ishmael was a witness to all their movements that morning, and a growing satisfaction began to be blended with the little animal's hate. He knew traps from many a firsthand experience, and to such as he a trap was a boon, not a menace — often turning up a double banquet, the bait and the baited.

All that day the Wyants kept diligently at their work setting out a fifteen-mile area, and until midday the old wolverine dogged their footsteps. Then he sought a hollow tree and slept, to be abroad again with the night.

Toward dusk, as the brothers were climbing out of a gloomy ravine in the valley bottom, an ancient half-dead pine called their attention by its great size. It was a hoary monarch of its kind, a couple of centuries old, and the only remnant of its day left in the region. Old rotting stumps showed how some long-ago fire had demolished its fellows. The bark was beginning to fall away in patches and half its boughs were bare and dead. A great hollow at its base showed the inroad many a fire had made into its heart.

The Wyants knelt and peered up into the dark hollow bole, ever

57

alert to discover some new secret of the forest. Jude, the younger, unslung a marten set and was preparing to plant it in the opening, when his brother's hand restrained him.

"Bear tree," Eben said. "Let be. We'll take a look at it again, come January."

Jude nodded.

"Bear'll hole up early this year," Eben predicted. "No mast. Sol Wire seen one over on the shoulder last week — hunger proud, asuckin' his paws."

The snow had begun to fall intermittently again as Ishmael went humping and slouching along the valley bottom that night. He was in search of a meal with a seasoning of devilish amusement thrown in, and he knew where the combination could be most easily found: along the Wyants' fresh-laid trap lines. In a ravine he came presently upon a marten set carefully buried in the brush and snow. He placed it to an inch, by the smell of iron that came up to him. Then he craftily dug about it, uncovered the chain, and fell to jerking it until the trap finally sprung, as he knew it would. His lips lifted and flickered as if in derision, as he squatted and devoured the bait.

Not satisfied with this, he vented his mean nature on the trap itself, entangling it in the brush so that half an hour of vexatious work would be necessary to unsnarl it. Then he passed on.

He came presently upon a weasel trap with a fresh-killed victim. A few brief minutes were occupied in tearing his tiny cousin from the trap and bolting him. Then he wrenched the trap from its fastenings and disappeared with it into the gloom of the forest. That trap was never found again.

The carcajou covered twenty miles that night in his depredations, and hardly a trap, snare or deadfall on the Wyants' line but was robbed, demolished or dragged away and buried, as his whim dictated. When daylight came he was curled up asleep on a rocky ledge.

That afternoon the Wyants covered the territory they had set out, and when they met at dusk at the farthest limit of their lines each had a sulphurous story to tell of the havoc that had been wrought.

"Injun devil," Jude muttered, and his brother nodded.

Nettled as they were over their losses, their wrath was not un-tempered with a degree of pleasure at the prospect of the game that loomed ahead. They set themselves at once to planning schemes of reprisal for the succeeding days.

"The varmint's old and wise," Eben said. "Git him at his own game, we will. Keep on asetting bait for a spell as if we thought we'd wear him down, then plant double sets, one with bait and one without. That ought to fetch him."

As the brothers turned homeward they talked in low tones of the plans for the morrow, stopping to reset the traps and snares that were not made useless by the carcajou.

"Think there might be two of them?" Jude asked.

"Two nothing! Ain't room in the woods for two o' him!" Eben said.

They talked like injured men, but a grim satisfaction grew upon them at the increasing evidence of the wolverine's sagacity. To Jude, at least, the prospect of a prolonged contest with the wiliest of all the forest dwellers was more edifying than the richest harvest of furs, for it helped to lift the unconscious loneliness and monotony of their forest life.

For a week thereafter the curious feud between the two men and the small quadruped continued, with the score of vantage continually mounting in favor of the wolverine.

The end of two weeks found the brothers sitting by their daubed clay fireplace finishing some final preparations against the little robber who by now had usurped their every waking thought. Six traps had been burned in the open fire to destroy every scent of iron or human hands. They handled the traps with mittens which had been treated with a solution of lye. Today they were to supplement each main set with a second unbaited trap.

59

That afternoon they made the rounds, using infinite care to preserve the unsullied appearance of the snow about each set. Early dusk that night found the old Injun devil abroad as usual, traversing the valley bottom in a particularly evil frame of mind. He had not slept well that day, and it was high time he found himself a permanent den against the growing cold.

Tonight as he approached the trap lines he exercised a greater caution than ever before, seemingly warned by an uncanny presage of the new menace awaiting him. Along the line were the fresh-made tracks of the Wyants' snowshoes, with which he now insolently blended his own, for he had become negligent on the matter of harm coming to him from the men themselves. But that careful camouflaging of the snow about the sets did not fool him.

The first set he came to, he robbed of two goodly chunks of frozen fish without mishap. A bit farther on the scent of dead grouse made him lick his muzzle hungrily. Beneath a spreading larch tree he viewed a curious-looking bark shelter built against the tree to keep the snow from the trap. Within the opening lay the grouse in a bed of feathers. Ishmael knew that danger lurked about so tempting a banquet. He circled the layout, studying it with savage eyes, and finally began an inch-by-inch approach, delicately testing every inch of the snow before putting his foot upon it. No smell of iron came to him until he was a foot away. The trap lay in the opening of the shelter. Cunningly he dug down to the chain, and in another minute the whole set lay uncovered. Carefully he pulled the thing aside, then scooped the dead bird into the open with a flick of his paw.

Almost at the same instant he leaped into the air with a calamitous squall of pain. Spinning round as he lighted, he tore desperately at the two steel jaws that had seized upon one hind foot in a deathly clamp.

For a moment panic ran down the dim aisles of the woods as the thief, bent double, whirled about in a mad fight to break the awful thing that clutched his foot. He clawed at it wildly, but the contraption held.

As there was obviously nothing to be gained by his frenzied efforts, Ishmael grew suddenly calm with a return of the cold, deadly acumen that made him what he was. He sat down in the snow and set his wits to work. If violent movement would not do it, try deliberate twists, reasoning out each move. For a long time he worked, but the steel teeth were inexorable.

There was a final recourse, a last desperate measure: to turn his own jaws upon the imprisoned foot. It would take all his stoic

60

courage but without flinching he proceeded; chewing through his own flesh and gristle and at last pulling free. Two toes had to be left behind him in the trap.

His predilection for trouble momentarily gone, Ishmael limped away, leaving a bloody trail. Toward the remote end of the valley he made his way, and before dawn came he found the sanctuary for which he sought. Among the tangled windfalls, relics of other centuries, one ancient pine tree still stood. At its base was a great hollow that ran up into the bole. Three feet up in the black interior he found a perfectly ordained shelf in the punky wood just large enough for him to curl up on. There, protected from the cold and wind, he fell into a deep healing sleep.

On the following day the Wyants viewed with a mixture of satisfaction and chagrin the near success of their stratagem.

"Pinches his toes for fair, that time," Eben said.

They studied the bloody signs in the snow.

"Try trackin' him," Eben said. "He'll hole up for a spell to heal."

They followed the blood-marked trail, but within an hour lost it completely in the hopeless tangle of the windfalls.

Throughout the week Ishmael remained curled up in his hollow tree while the clean air and prolonged sleep performed their healing work. The fifth day saw the flesh and sinews of his foot knit once more, though the remaining toes had fallen away and the smooth stump of his leg bone protruded. He would always limp but his indomitable courage and arrogance were dampened not a whit. When he walked forth at the end of a week it was, if possible, in a still more indurated spirit of deviltry.

Craving strong rich food he made straight for the Wyants' trap lines. At trap after trap he stopped to stuff himself with meat. After his capacity had been reached he continued the rounds for the mere saturnalia of ruin he was able to wreak.

So involved was he in his game that he lingered on well into the morning. Suddenly, the dry crunching of the snow heralded the approach of the Wyants, and he tarried to watch them. As it happened, the catch of the night before had been the richest of the season. Not only had Ishmael avoided every snare they had planted for him, but his work of destruction had been complete.

No talk was wasted between the brothers as they turned homeward to prepare for a relentless hunt. Ishmael, from his covert, watched them go.

Sometime later as he was nearing his hollow tree for a day's sleep, he suddenly stopped short in the blowdowns to test the breeze. A sharp but indefinable warning had impressed his superacute senses, coming how or from where it could not be said. For no definite reason he changed his idea of sleeping and continued on down the valley, moving at his best limping pace. He did not suspect that less than a mile behind him the Wyants were gliding along on his fresh trail on their ten-foot whispering skis, on which they had more than once run down a fleeing fox. At first he did not suspect it. Then, though the wind was against him, an intimation came. It was a faint sound that came to him as Jude made a flying jump, a kind of *chug* and a soft tearing slither. Soon afterward he had a fleeting glimpse of his trailers as they flitted across the open space far to the rear. A low thick hiss came from the carcajou and thereafter he climbed whenever he could, and kept climbing, with an instinctive knowledge of the vantage gained.

The time that the Wyants lost climbing out of the valley was quickly regained along the windswept ridges. The third hour almost saw the finish of the desperate game. As the carcajou shuffled along a rock ledge, lips flecked with foam from his tremendous exertions, there came a skimming flight as of birds as the two men swept after him on the downgrade. Ishmael whirled, then flung himself blindly over the rocky ledge into space, and the quick-aimed bullets went

63

wild as the hunters flashed by. Ishmael hurtled downward forty feet onto another snowy ledge, bounced over it and went bounding down until he was lost to sight in the shadows of the young evergreens that choked the gorge below. The Wyants loved life better than he, for they did not attempt to follow.

Once more they were forced to turn homeward empty-handed.

Ishmael, from the opposite side of the valley, had watched them go, and then doggedly set out after them, his goal being no less than his home tree.

That night the wind increased steadily and by midnight the temperature had fallen twenty degrees. Ishmael's repose was troubled by many unaccustomed forest noises as the gale played havoc around him. His own tree swayed and groaned deep down in its fibers as the blasts tugged at its mighty roots. The once iron heart of the old pine was soft and riven from the ravages of a half century of decay and a myriad of boring insects.

The clock of the wilderness timed the end just a few minutes after Ishmael emerged the following morning in answer to the spur of his empty stomach — and with a deep-laid purpose. A fusillade of mighty snappings from the overwrought wood ran through the forest like a volley of rifle fire as the fibers at the giant's base began to part; the two-hundred-foot crown swayed and staggered. Then with an inanimate moaning sound the monarch careened and fell crashing.

The far-reaching thunder of its final descent caught Ishmael in his tracks a quarter of a mile down the valley, and he left off eating a captured grouse to listen. In its fall the giant roots of the pine had torn up an excavation in the earth, big as a bomb pit. Presently, among the tangled roots and earth, a startling movement might have been seen. It was as if the great scar in the earth were given birth to an apparition, as a gaunt old female bear emerged from the hole — none other than Ishmael's old-time enemy.

Weeks before, at the beginning of the first snow, the she-bear had come upon the blasted pine as had Ishmael, and chosen it for her winter hibernation. Deep down among the roots below ground, she had dug a den for herself, and the end of the first month of her mysterious sleep had found her covered over with a blanket of drifted snow some two feet thick. When Ishmael had chosen the hollow tree for sanctuary two months later, the winter storms had effectively covered every trace and scent of the sleeping occupant.

The great tree's fall had partially uncovered the bear's den, and it had been the ruthless sting of the knife-edged wind that finally roused her from her deathlike torpor. Her rest had been poor at best. Thanks to Ishmael, her almost human sorrowing over her murdered cub had worn her thin in the fall, and she had failed to put on the necessary blanket of fat against the long sleep. Now that her den had been destroyed, she was doomed to wander homeless and miserable, seeking what scanty sustenance could be found in the winter woods till spring broke the clamp of famine. Knowledge of this, combined with her rude awakening, had roused the old she-bear to a demoniac rage. No sooner had she emerged from her hole than she came upon the fresh trail of Ishmael, the creature she had come to hate above all living things.

A low rumbling note of anger issued from deep down in the old mother's chest as she stood, head swaying, testing the wind. Gaunt as a specter, she looked like the spirit of vengeance as she swung about and shambled away on the trail Ishmael had left.

About half an hour later Ishmael himself returned, coming from the opposite direction. A vague sense of something wrong prompted caution as he approached the spot, and the appalling sight of the great conifer lying prone along the hillside gripped him for a minute in a spell of awe and terror. Then he came upon the fresh tracks of the she-bear. The hair rose stiffly along his spine at the familiar, frightening scent.

Along the prostrate trunk of the great pine he shambled, savage, bewildered. Except that it had fallen, the tree seemed still intact. There was the hollow at its base, easy of access and a good sanctuary still. It was as he was peering within, that the old she-bear emerged from the woods scarcely a hundred feet distant. Before she had made him out Ishmael slipped quickly into the hollow of the bole. The hole, he knew, was too small to admit her great bulk.

Soon the body of the old mother darkened the hole opening. Her nose told her Ishmael was within, and grimly, relentlessly, she set to work tearing her way into his retreat.

That night the Wyant brothers sat talking by their fire, conversation as usual pivoting around the evil little genius, when mention was made of the hollow pine they had discovered early in the fall. As they talked, a conviction began to grow upon them that they had hit upon the secret of the old carcajou's winter retreat.

The first light found them traversing the valley bottom on their

65

snowshoes. The storm had abated in the night. When they searched the sky line for the towering crown of the king pine that had formerly stood out as a landmark, and found it gone, they doubled their pace. It was not long before they were standing beside the fallen monarch, wordless as they deciphered the intricate story written in the snow. Down by the roots of the tree they found a flattened furry form, torn, battered and literally shredded into strips all that was left of Ishmael, the indomitable. Round about were signs of a battle that had been waged with a bear — a beast at least fifteen times his size and weight, and those signs told of no one-sided fray. The trail of the bear that led down the valley was marked by carmine splashes.

"They fought," Jude said, in something like awe, and either brother would have given his finest pelt to have witnessed the thing. "The little critter was cornered in the hole, an' lit into the bear at the end, like a nest of red devils!"

The thing that puzzled them was the reason back of the bear's relentless fury.

"Musta had a grudge agin him, like ourselves," Eben said. "He's done for, but it's no credit to us. He had us fair stumped at every turn of the game; I'll give that to him, the little cuss, an' he was the one critter of the woods that could of done it. Reckon he went out with full honors, too, for his size."

Something of the same mystical fancy that makes the far northern Indians covet a garment of carcajou fur as an aid to craft and bravery prompted Jude's remark:

"Got me a job to do, 'fore I'm done with trapping. Ketch me a prime devil fur."

STRIPES, THE UNCONCERNED

by Charles G. D. Roberts

By curious coincidence, in Canada, in the same year — 1860 — were born two men, Charles G. D. Roberts and Ernest Thompson Seton, destined to live long lives (Roberts died at eighty-three, Seton at eighty-six), each to be remembered for his animal stories for young readers.

Roberts, both an athlete and a scholar, left a teaching career in Nova Scotia to devote his energies to writing. He produced some fifty books, among them *The Kindred of the Wild*, *Hoof and Claw*, and *Jim, the Story of a Backwoods Police Dog*. From this last work comes the following story of a skunk he calls "Stripes".

On the edge of evening, when the last of the light was gathered in the pale-green upper sky, and all the world of the quiet backwoods clearings was sunken in a soft violet dusk, a leisurely and self-possessed little animal came strolling among the ancient stumps and mossy hillocks of the open upland sheep-pasture. He was about the size of an average cat, but shorter of leg, with a long, sharp-muzzled head, and he carried his broad feathery tail very high in a graceful arch, like a squirrel in good humour. Unlike most other creatures of the wild, his colouring was such as to make him conspicuous rather than to conceal him. He was black, with a white stripe down his face, a white patch on the back of his neck, and a white stripe all the way along each side of his body. And, also, unlike the rest of the furtive folk, he seemed quite unconcerned to hide his movements from observation. Neither was he for ever glancing this way and that, as if on the watch for enemies. Rather he had the air of being content that his enemies should do the watching—and avoid him.

The skunk — for such was the undignified appellation of this very dignified personality of the wilderness — was pleasantly engrossed in his own business. That business, at the moment, consisted in catching the big, fat, juicy, copper-brown "June-bugs" as they emerged from their holes in the sod, crawled up the bending grass-stems, and spread their wings for their heavy evening flight. It was easy hunting, and he had no need of haste. To snap up these great, slow and clumsy beetles as they clung upon the grass-stems was as easy as picking strawberries, and, indeed, not altogether dissimilar, as he would nip off the hard, glossy wing-cases of the big beetles as one nips off the hull of the berry before munching the succulent morsel.

68

Having slept the day through in his snug burrow, in the under-brush which fringed the forest edge of the clearing, he had come forth into the dewy twilight equipped with a fine appetite. He had come with the definite purpose of hunting "June-bugs," this being the season, all too brief, for that highly-flavoured delicacy. At first he had thought of nothing else; but when he had taken the edge off his hunger, he began to consider the chances of varying his diet. As he seized an unlucky beetle, close to the edge of a flat, spreading juniper bush, a brooding ground-sparrow flew up, with a startled *cheep*, from under his very nose. He dropped the beetle and made a lightning pounce at the bird. But her wing had flicked him across the eyes, confusingly, and he missed her. He knew well enough, however, what her presence there among the warm grass-tussocks meant. He went nosing eagerly under the juniper bush, and soon found a nest with four little brown-mottled eggs in it. Tiny though they were, they made a tit-bit very much to his taste, all the more so that they were very near hatching. Having licked his jaws and fastidiously polished the fur of his shrewd, keen face, he sauntered off to see what other delicacies the evening might have in store for him.

A little further on, toward the centre of the pasture, he came upon a flat slab of rock, its surface sloping toward the south, its southward edge slightly overhanging and fringed with soft grass. He knew the rock well — knew how its bare surface drank in the summer sun all day long, and held the warmth throughout the dew-chill nights. He knew, too, that other creatures besides himself might very well appreciate this genial warmth. Stealthily, and without the smallest disturbance of the grassy fringe, he sniffed along the overhanging edge of the rock. Suddenly he stiffened, and his sharp nose darted in under the rock. Then he jerked back, with the writhing tail of a snake between his jaws.

The prize was a big black-and-yellow garter snake, not far from three feet long, — not venomous, but full of energy and fight. It tried to cling to its hiding-place; but the shrewd skunk, instead of attempting to pull it out straight, like a cork from a bottle neck, ran forward a pace or two, and, as it were, "peeled" it forth. It doubled out, struck him smartly in the face with its harmless fangs, and then coiled itself about his neck and forelegs. There was a moment of confused rough-and-tumble, but the skunk knew just how to handle this kind of antagonist. Having bitten the reptile's

tail clean through, he presently, with the help of his practised little jaws, succeeded in getting hold of it by the back, an inch or two behind the head. This ended the affair, as a struggle, and the victor proceeded to round off his supper on snake. He managed to put away almost all but the head and tail, and then, after a meticulous toilet to fur and paws — for he was as fastidiously clean as a cat — he sauntered back toward his burrow in the underbrush, to refresh himself with a nap before seeking further adventures.

Directly in his path stood three or four young seedling firs, about two feet high, in a dense cluster. Half a dozen paces beyond this tiny thicket a big red fox, belly to earth, was soundlessly stalking some quarry, perhaps a mouse, which could be heard ever so faintly rustling the grass-stems at the edge of the thicket. To the skunk, with his well-filled belly, the sound had no interest. He rounded the thicket and came face to face with the fox.

Neither in size, strength, nor agility was he any match for the savage red beast which stood in his path, and was quite capable, indeed, of dispatching him in two snaps of his long, lean jaws. But he was not in the least put out. Watchful, but cool, he kept straight on, neither delaying nor hastening his leisurely and nonchalant progress. The fox, on the other hand, stopped short. He was hungry. His hunting was interfered with, for that rustling under the fir-branches had stopped. His fine red brush twitched angrily. Nevertheless, he had no stomach to tackle this easy-going little gentleman in the black-and-white stripes. Showing his long white teeth in a vindictive but noiseless snarl, he stepped aside. And the skunk, glancing back with bright eyes of vigilance and understanding, passed on as if the twilight world belonged to him. He knew — and he knew his enemy knew as well — that he carried with him a concealed weapon of such potency that no fox, unless afflicted with madness, would ever willingly run up against it.

Reaching his burrow in the underbrush without further adventure, he found it empty. His mate and her young ones — now three-quarters grown — were scattered away foraging for themselves over the wide, forest-scented clearings. It was a spacious burrow, dug by a sturdy, surly old woodchuck, who, though usually as pugnacious as a badger and an obstinate stickler for his rights, had in this case yielded without a fight to the mild-mannered little usurper, and humped off in disgust to hollow a new abode much deeper in the forest, where such a mischance would not be likely to happen to

71

him again. Under the tenancy of the skunk family the burrow was sweet and dry and daintily kept. With a little grumble of content deep in his throat he curled himself up and went to sleep.

When he woke and set forth again to renew his foraging, although he had only slept an hour, his vigorous digestion had quite restored his appetite. He had no more thought for "June-bugs." He wanted bigger game, more red-blooded and with some excitement in it. He thought of the farmyard, half a mile away across the clearings, down over the round of the upland. It was weeks now since he had visited it. There might be something worth picking up. There might be a mother hen with chickens, in a pen which he could find a way into. There might be a hen sitting on her clutch of eggs in a stolen nest under the barn. He had discovered in previous seasons that most sitting hens had their nests provided for them in secure places which he could in no way manage to come at. But he had also found that sometimes a foolish and secretive — and very young — hen will *hide* her nest in some such out-of-the-way place as under the barn floor, where the troublesome human creatures who preside over the destinies of hens cannot get at it. Here she keeps her precious eggs all to herself till she has enough to cover comfortably, and then she proceeds to the pleasant task of brooding them, and has things all her own way till some night-prowler comes along and convicts her, finally and fatally, of her folly.

A full moon, large and ruddy like a ripe pumpkin, was just rising behind the jagged black tops of the spruce forest. It threw long, fantastic, confusing shadows across the dewy hillocks of the pasture. Hither and thither, in and out and across the barred streaks of light, darted the wild rabbits, gambolling as if half beside themselves, as if smitten with a midsummer madness by the capricious magic of the night. But if mad, they retained enough sound sense to keep ever at a prudent distance from the leisurely striped wayfarer who appeared so little interested in their sport. Though they were bigger than he, they knew that, if they should venture within reach of his pounce, his indifference would vanish and his inexorable fangs would be in their throats.

Knowing his utter inability to compete with the speed of the rabbits, now they were wide awake, the skunk hardly noticed their antics, but kept on his direct path toward the farmyard. Presently, however, his attention was caught by the rabbits scattering off in every direction. On the instant he was all alert for the cause. Mount-

ing a hillock, he caught sight of a biggish shaggy-haired dog some distance down the pasture. The dog was racing this way and that as crazily, it seemed, as the rabbits, with faint little yelps of excitement and whines of disappointment. He was chasing the rabbits with all his energy; and it was evident that he was a stranger, a new-comer to the wilderness world, for he seemed to think he might hope to catch the fleet-foot creatures by merely running after them. As a matter of fact, he had just arrived that same day at the backwoods farm from the city down the river. His experience had been confined to streets and gardens and the chasing of cats, and he was daft with delight over the spacious freedom of the clearings. The skunk eyed him scornfully, and continued his journey with the unconcern of an elephant.

A moment later the dog was aware of a little, insignificant black-and-white creature coming slowly towards him as if unconscious of his presence. Another rabbit! But as this one did not seem alarmed, he stopped and eyed it with surprise, his head cocked to one side in inquiry. The skunk half turned and moved off slowly, deliberately, at right angles to the path he had been following.

With a yelp of delight the dog dashed at this easy victim, which seemed so stupid that it made no effort to escape. He was almost upon it. Another leap and he would have had it in his jaws. But the amazing little animal turned its back on him, stuck its tail straight in the air, and jerked up its hindquarters with a derisive gesture. In that instant something hot and soft struck the inexperienced hunter full in the face — something soft, indeed, but overwhelming, paralyzing. It stopped him dead in his tracks. Suffocating, intolerably

73

pungent, it both blinded him and choked him. His lungs refused to work, shutting up spasmodically. Gasping and gagging, he grovelled on his belly and strove frantically to paw his mouth and nostrils clear of the dense, viscous fluid which was clogging them. Failing in this, he fell to rooting violently in the short grass, biting and tearing at it and rolling in it, till some measure of breath and eyesight returned to him.

Thereupon, his matted head all stuck with grass and moss and dirt, he set off racing madly for the farmhouse where he expected to get relief from the strange torment which afflicted him. But when he pawed and whined at the kitchen door for admittance, he was

driven off with contumely and broomsticks. There was nothing for him to do but slink away with his shame to a secluded corner between the wagon-shed and the pig-pen, where he could soothe his burning muzzle in the cool winds and fresh earth. On the following day one of the farm hands, with rude hands and unsympathetic comment, scrubbed him violently with liquid soap and then clipped close his splendid shaggy coat. But it was a week before he was readmitted to the comfortable fellowship of the farmhouse kitchen.

For a moment or two, with a glance of triumph in his bright eyes, the skunk had watched the paroxysms of his discomfited foe. Then, dropping the tip of his tail into its customary disdainful arch, he had turned back towards his burrow. This was a redoubtable foe whom he had just put to rout, and he had expended most of his armoury upon him. He had no wish to risk another encounter until the potent secretion which he carried in a sac between the powerful muscles of his thighs should have had time to accumulate again. He dropped for that night, all notion of the distinctly adventurous expedition to the farmyard, contenting himself with snapping up a few beetles and crickets as he went. He was lucky enough to pounce upon an indiscreet field-mouse just as she emerged from her burrow, and then a few minutes' digging with his powerful and expert fore-paws had served to unearth the mouse's nest with her half-dozen tiny blind sucklings. So he went home well satisfied with himself.

Before re-entering he again made a careful toilet; and as the opening of the sac from which he had projected the potent fluid into his enemy's face had immediately closed up tight and fast, he carried no trace of the virulent odour with him. Indeed, that fluid was a thing which he never by any chance allowed to get on to his own fur. Always, at the moment of ejecting it, the fur on his thighs parted and lay back flat to either side of the naked vent of the sac, and the long tail cocked itself up rigidly, well out of the way. It was a stuff he kept strictly for his foes, and never allowed to offend either himself or his friends.

On entering his burrow he found there his mate and all the youngsters, curled up together in the sleep of good digestion and easy conscience. He curled himself up with them, that the supply of his high-explosive might accumulate during another forty winks.

About an hour before the dawn he awoke again, feeling hungry. The rest of the family were still sleeping, having gorged themselves, as he might have done had it not been for that encounter with the misguided dog. He left them whimpering contentedly in their cosy slumber, and crept forth into the dewy chill alone, his heart set on mice and suchlike warm-blooded game.

The moon was now high overhead, sailing honey-coloured through a faintly violet sky. The rough pasture, with its stumps and hillocks, was touched into a land of dream.

76

Now, it chanced that an old bear, who was accustomed to foraging in the valley beyond the cedar swamp, had on this night decided to bring her cub on an expedition toward the more dangerous neighbourhood of the clearings. She wanted to begin his education in all the wariness which is so necessary for the creatures of the wild in approaching the works and haunts of man. On reaching the leafy fringe of bushes which fringed the rude rail-fence dividing the forest from the pasture, she cautiously poked her head through the leafage, and for perhaps a minute, motionless as a stone, she interrogated the bright open spaces with eyes and ears and nostrils. The cub, taking the cue from his mother, stiffened to the like movelessness at her side, his bright little eyes full of interest and curiosity. There was no sign of danger in the pasture. In fact, there were the merry rabbits hopping about in the moonlight undisturbed. This was a sign of security quite good enough for the wise old bear. With crafty and experienced paws she forced a hole in the fence — leaving the top rail, above the binder, in its place — and led the eager cub forth into the moonlight.

The special notion of the bear in coming to the pasture was to teach her cub the art of finding, unearthing, and catching the toothsome wild mice. Keeping along near the fence, she sniffed the tussocky, uneven grass with practised nose. But the first thing she came upon was a bumble-bees' nest. This was far more to her taste than any mice. She gave a low call to the cub; but the cub was preoccupied now, sniffing at the rabbit tracks, and lifting himself on his hindquarters to stare longingly at the rabbits, who were hopping off to discreeter distance. The mother did not insist on his coming to watch her tackle the bees' nest. After all, he was perhaps a bit young to face the stings of the angry bees, and she might as well have the little hoard of honey and larvae and beebread for herself. The cub wandered off a little way, with some vague notion of chasing the elusive rabbits.

Just then through the edge of the underbrush appeared the skunk, stretching himself luxuriously before he started off across the pasture. He saw the bear, but he knew that sagacious beast would pay him no attention whatever. He trotted out into the moonlight and pounced upon a fat black cricket as an appetizer.

The cub caught sight of the pretty little striped creature, and came darting clumsily and gaily to the attack. He would show his mother that he could do some hunting on his own account. The striped creature turned its back on him and moved off slowly. The cub was delighted. He was just going to reach out a rude little paw and grab the easy prize. Then the inevitable happened. The pretty striped creature gave its stern a contemptuous jerk, and the deluded cub fell in a heap, squealing, gasping, choking, and pawing convulsively at the horrible sticky stuff which filled his mouth and eyes.

Just before the catastrophe occurred, the old bear had looked up from her business with the bees, and had uttered a loud *woof* of warning. But too late. The last thing in the world she wanted to do was to try any fooling with a skunk. But now her rage at the suffering and discomfiture of her little one swept away all prudence. With a grunt of fury she charged at the offender. One glance at the approaching vengeance convinced the skunk that this time he had made a mistake. He turned and raced for the underbrush as fast as his little legs would carry him. But that was not fast enough. Just as he was about to dart under the fence, a huge black paw, shod with claws like steel, crashed down upon him, and his leisurely career came to an end.

The bear, in deep disgust, scraped her reeking paw long and earnestly in the fresh earth beneath the grass, then turned her attention to the unhappy cub. She relieved her feelings by giving him a sharp cuff which sent him sprawling a dozen feet. Then, relenting, she showed him how to clean himself by rooting in the earth. At length, when he could see and breathe once more with some degree of comfort, she indignantly led him away back into the depths of the consoling forest.

A MAN-MADE WATER HOLE

by Mary L. Jobe Akeley

In the midst of a great city it is possible suddenly to walk into a jungle full of wild animals. The city is New York, and the jungle stretches through the Akeley African Hall of the American Museum of Natural History, so realistically that it seems as if in a minute the lions will roar, the deer will run away. Carl Akeley, hunter and naturalist, went on expeditions expressly to get these "specimens" for the Museum. His wife, Mary L. Jobe Akeley, has written of their adventures together in their book, *In the African Jungle*. Here, in an excerpt from that book, she tells how, without being seen, they were able to watch creatures both shy and fierce.

While Carl and I were hunting giraffe in northern Kenya, we witnessed this drought and its attendant migration. Because of it and because necessity is the mother of invention, my husband evolved a plan to keep the game within the neighbourhood of our camp — a plan that to my knowledge had never been tried before.

He would rebuild the water hole! Perhaps the game would come again to drink. Taking with us a dozen natives, each bearing sharp *pangas* (knives), he set them to work scooping out the hole to a depth of eighteen inches. In the excavation Carl placed a large linen tarpaulin, covering the edge carefully with some of the clay that had been removed in the digging. Then he filled the freshly dug pan with water from an old saline well near our camp after making sure that it was safe to do so. We carried to our improvised water hole more than a hundred gallons of the precious liquid.

On the day following the building and filling of the artificial pool, our excitement was intense. Would thirst lure the herds back again? The success or failure of our practical test would be decided within a very short time. We hoped, watched and waited.

In the morning a fair number of antelope and zebra came in and drank. That was encouraging. We hauled out more water and kept the pool well supplied. Then we set out on our regular daily search for giraffe. As the hours passed, belief became conviction — something was holding our long-necked friends. It even seemed that they were more numerous than they had been on the preceding day. By evening it had become certain that the game in the district had scented the water and had decided to remain. Our venture was a success!

We were tremendously elated, and at sunset Carl came to me with eyes shining.

"How would you like to sleep by the water hole tonight?" he asked.

"Would I? Just give me the chance," I replied.

He had pulled together an old thorn blind that had been used three or four years before by another game observer, and reconstructed it within a few yards of the water pan. At twilight, when ready for the night's adventure, we prepared to take our position in the blind.

As the moments crawled along, the very air seemed freighted with the tenseness of approaching events. We, the hidden watchers, knew that our experiment was successful — but we did not know what adventures it might involve. Miles away, thirsty beasts had scented the water. Through the bush and across the plains, nostrils were dilated, sniffing the wind to catch the direction of our improvised well. Many feet were moving instinctively and steadily toward us. Eyes — gentle or fierce — were guiding their owners closer. We were being surrounded by a tightening ring of wild creatures.

In the semi-blackness before our "front-row" seats, the show was now beginning. Carl was kneeling with his eyes at the peep-hole. Something was certainly happening. The patter of light feet resounded on the baked clay outside. Quickly and quietly as I could, I got on my knees and crawled to my own lookout. It was possible to see a little outside in the star light of the great constellations overspreading the vast domed sky.

Small, shadowy shapes gathered about the brink of the water hole — Grant's gazelle. Among the most beautiful of all antelopes,

their graceful bodies merged and blended in the faint light like a
fantastic moving cloud. Next came the clatter of many zebra hoofs —
heavy, rhythmic, like a galloping of mustangs — and the Grants
were driven from their recently discovered treasure. The harsh
deep call of the Grevy zebra stallions was unmistakable. Snorting
and gulping, they took immediate possession of the water hole.
A half dozen oryx soon followed, trotting in liesurely and drinking

with the zebra, in the same friendly manner in which they are accustomed to graze together in their pasture lands. They are so well matched, in size and strength, fleetness and fighting ability, that there is no conflict between them. As though blessing Carl's improvised water hole, they guzzled and talked to each other. Maybe they wondered at their good luck, but it is more likely that they simply accepted without question that which fate had brought to them.

Soon they stopped drinking, sniffed and snorted a little, and then made off across the veldt. The echo of their hoofs was still audible when we heard a new and distinct sound. We crawled nearer to our peep-holes — scratching ourselves anew with the thorns, in our eagerness to watch the entrance of this important actor. A huge leaden shadow loomed out of the greater shadow of the night.

A most extraordinary noise now began. Snorting, pawing, gulping, grunting, guzzling, the newcomer made himself entirely at home in our water pan. It could not survive long, the way the big fellow was trampling it about. Only one creature could be guilty of such bad manners — old rough-and-ready rhino.

Suddenly a hyena set up his doleful yodel, and jackals ran barking into the night as the shambling monster came into our line of vision. Beheld under such circumstances, the rhino was even more strange, more reminiscent of some prehistoric monster, than he had ever been when viewed in the sane sunlight. He was like some phantom in a dream, with his incredible head and astonishing bulk etched against a faintly illuminated world.

Apparently our huge visitor did not suspect that he was being observed. Several times his ugly snout and vicious double horn were pointed straight in our direction, but the rhino, unlike almost all other animals, acts as if he were wholly unafraid, and never resorts to the caution and wariness practiced by many other beasts. There was little possibility of his seeing or hearing us, as a rhino's eyes are not of the keenest, and he was making too much noise himself to detect the faint sound of our movements. Still, there remained a strong likelihood that he would get our scent. If that happened, trouble was headed our way. Our interest and excitement were too great to let us worry about a little thing like a couple of tons of rhino, and apparently he was too content with his discovery of the water to bother about any humans who might possibly be in the neighborhood. Into the pool he plowed and splashed — head, foot, hood and hide!

Unfortunately the rhino is not a dainty drinker, and our visitor seemed determined to live up to — or down to — the reputation of his family. While he drank he wallowed, and while he wallowed he ruined our beautiful water hole which had been built with so much labor and care in the hope of keeping the game near us for many days. We watched this operation with mixed emotions. We were altogether willing to have an opportunity to study this great beast unobserved and at such close range, but we could not help feeling sorry that our smaller and more polite friends would find nothing on the morrow but a muddy mess when they came in for their morning drink. Their disappointment would be ours as well, for they would immediately leave the vicinity of camp and we would see them no more.

When the east grew faintly streaked with dawn, giving us a better view of our surroundings, we crawled out of our thorny refuge, startling a colony of golden feathered weaver birds in their nests in the acacia overhead. A whirr of wings, a skyward rush, and the hornbills, roosting near the pool, took to flight, their over-sized beaks opening to emit their harsh and jarring cries. We were just in time to disturb a flock of sand grouse drifting in to seek the water that had slaked their thirst the day before — this time, alas, only to find destruction and disappointment.

All the way back to camp the plains were dotted with the friendly little wild folk who had given us our night's entertainment — antelope, zebra, oryx, soon to vanish in the perpetual quest of water. They, too, had enjoyed a new experience, had they but known it, in drinking from a man-made water hole.

A PAIR OF KINGS

by *Raymond Lee Ditmars*

While the late Dr. Raymond L. Ditmars was Curator of the New York Zoological Park, he received many calls for help. Though he went to the rescue of baboons and whatever other animals (or their keepers!) who needed him, he most expertly knew and dealt with snakes. Here Ditmars tells how he and an assistant got into and out of an unexpectedly tight corner, in this exciting chapter from *Strange Animals I Have Known*.

One morning I received a telephone call from one of the older animal dealers whose disordered gloomy places are fast disappearing. The man was excited and urged me to hurry down, that he had two big king cobras loose. We wanted to buy a pair of these creatures but I didn't relish the job of capturing them. Nevertheless the head-keeper and I started down. We carried a large fibre satchel in which were two deep, burlap bags, and a staff with a noose at the end.

The king cobra holds the palm as the largest and most active of all poisonous serpents. It grows to be fifteen feet long and is built like a great whip. From its size and extremely deadly venom it is by far the most formidable of any serpent. But added to all this is its curiously alert mentality or intelligence, and its common habit of deliberately pursuing and attacking humans. It is Indo-Malayan and fortunately not generally common.

We found the dealer in a bad state of excitement. He had had a shipment of birds from India and among the cages was a large case of the usual Oriental teakwood with a few holes at the top. It was heavy and he had carried it up to a room where he broke up boxes and cages, intending to knock off the top and carry the "python" it appeared to contain to the downstairs snake cages. As he expected to find a twelve to fifteen footer, stupid on being exposed to the light after its long journey, he anticipated no trouble in two men carrying the beast — one at the head and another at the tail — leaving the box behind to be broken up.

He knocked off part of the cover and at the first glance was surprised to see so much space in the case. He expected to find the highly piled coils of the Indian python. The weight of the case had deceived him, as teak is very heavy. Another look told the story. There were many loops of pale olive, no thicker than a man's wrist.

As the dealer brandished the hammer in fright, an orange-coloured head with glowing eyes rose straight up. He backed for the door and the apparition continued to rise directly upward until the cobra had reared to the level of the man's breast, giving him a fearless preparatory stare.

By this time the man had retreated through the door, stepping on the feet of the assistant who had come to help him. They both fell backward against the balustrade in the dark hallway. Just as the dealer closed the door he caught the flash of a second cobra rearing beside the first, the two like great candlesticks. And they stared venomously at him!

I know only too well that curious stare of the king cobra. Its eyes are strangely brilliant — not luminous — but *alert*. The stare is piercing, as if to analyze and anticipate one's moves. The colour of the reptile's eyes usually matches the hue of its throat and head which are of ruddy yellow like an orange skin, giving the anterior portion of the snake distinct character in contrast to the pale olive body.

The dealer was terrified that the snakes would escape. There were two windows in the room, but they were safe because the place had been used for transferring large birds and the sashes were covered with fine but strong mesh, cut in panels stapled over the entire casing from top to bottom. The room, however, was about eighteen feet square, and it was filled with trash, broken boxes and their covers, which were piled waist and shoulder high. There were rats in the old building and the floor of the room had not been examined for years, owing to the litter. The dealer feared that rats might have gnawed through the floor to make a meeting place of the room and to enlarge their travelling channels. If so, the cobras could escape into the building. He wrung his hands at the thought of king cobras at liberty in downtown New York and implored me to get busy. I'll confess that right there I was somewhat apprehensive about going up to that room.

The first thing the dealer did was to take a key from his pocket and unlock the door. Then he backed off while we peeked in. There was nothing in sight. Fortunately, there was some cleared space on our side. The door swung inward and jammed on the floor when half way opened. I momentarily closed it to make more room. There was a stout piece of wooden strip loose on the floor which the head keeper appropriated as a staff. We had the two burlap bags and the stick with the noose.

89

Next we cautiously peered around, gently shoving a broken box here and there before we saw the first snake. A greenish fold protruded from beneath a case. The cobra was asleep. But I knew what he would do if we touched him: boil out from the shelter and rear in combat attitude, possibly come right at us. However, I figured we could handle him with the two sticks if the second cobra didn't join the party.

"Go around behind me and open the door so we have a getaway; I'm going to stir him up!" I cautioned the head-keeper. He quietly moved behind me and grasped the handle. *The door was locked!*

My anger at the cowardly dealer for locking us in was hard to repress. But I had to grind my teeth and knock softly at the door. We didn't dare start any vibration by kicking it. There was no response. It was probable that the man was cowering downstairs.

We were in a fine mess! The door was too stout to be kicked through and the windows were covered with mesh. I told my companion not to hesitate, but swing hard and disable the cobre if he came at us. As there was nothing to do but start I poked the greenish coil.

Instantly there was a hiss like a muffled sneeze, deeper in tone than the characteristic sneezing hiss of the common Indian cobra — and out and up the serpent came, turning to us with his intent stare. His neck slowly expanded into the long narrow hood of his species, showing black and white spots between the scales.

That slow expanding of the hood was a favourable sign. The snake was hesitating between anger and surprise. I knew that here was the critical moment to get him. If the noose didn't work he would get one of us — or there would be a dead cobra.

My assistant slowly waggled his stick as I reached forward and upward with the noose. I saw the cobra's intent eyes give a flicking glance at the noose. There was also a slight movement of his head. But instantly, the eyes gathered intensity in their gaze at me. Quickly the thin noose slipped over his head. But still he didn't move. A side

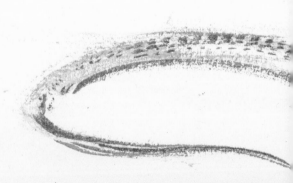

swing of the pole tightened the noose and we pulled him down, the constricting cord narrowing his hood about three inches from the head.

The way that long body poured out from under the boxes was terrifying. There were fully twelve feet of him. He furiously chewed the stick, embedding his fangs again and again in it. When my assistant got his stick across the snake's head I grasped the brute by the neck. This is not so dangerous as it sounds if one knows how to do it. The idea was to back him into our bag. Meanwhile he was raising an awful rumpus in the room, throwing his body around and crashing over boxes right and left. I yanked my end toward a corner, the other man pulling the serpent hand over hand to the bag, then starting to shove the tail portion in.

We were successfully backing our first cobra in when we saw the other one. Impressions are sometimes instantaneous. I remember now that the throat markings were different and I realized the two were a pair. She gave us more of a shock than the first, being high on the boxes and rearing fully four feet besides. She looked balefully over the scene like an avenger about to descend.

"Swing for that one!" I shouted, gathering the bag around the first snake. He was helping, if anything, in backing into the bag in his effort to pull his head away. Catching the edge of the bag I waited for him to yank back hard — and when he did I let go. It was a fifty-fifty chance. He might have shot out like a rocket; but he didn't and he was not given an instant's handicap. There is a way of letting go such a bag with one hand and spinning it with the other that instantly seals the serpent inside. I learned this years before and had taught it to all the keepers of the Reptile Department. The trick caught His Majesty by surprise and gave us two or three minutes leeway before he could push his head past the twists. All this was happening in less time than it takes to tell it.

At this moment there was an awful clatter beside me. It was my assistant trying to hold down the head and neck of the second snake. Now it was my turn to waggle the noose staff and stand ready. The lady pulled loose once and made a magnificent sweep at us, but missed by a couple of feet. We nearly climbed the wall in our scrambling jumps to duck that strike. A cobra doesn't strike like a viper, the latter being so quick there is a mere flash in the action. The king cobra sweeps forward in its strike and by a jump you can evade the movement if it isn't followed.

Now it was the cobra or ourselves and I was prepared to end it with a kill when the head-keeper made a swing between a blow and a push and pinned the creature's neck against the top of a tilting case. The case lay fairly firm. I followed this by jamming the noosing staff nearer the head and holding with all my strength as she lashed and whipped her body all around the room.

"I have a good grip — pin the head!" I yelled. My man's stick advanced over the head. All at once we had her, grasped firmly by the neck like the first. Here was victory! By using his knee to lever the stick in down pressure, he pinioned her with one hand and grasped her with the other.

With my assistant now holding the snake's neck in a two-fisted grip and half squatting on the reptile's anterior quarter, I tied the first bag. During the action with the lady cobra, it had been rising and pitching from side to side like a drunken thing. We backed number two into a bag, which was a lively but not difficult act as there was nothing else to bother us.

The next thing for us to do was to get the heaviest piece of wood in the room and batter down that infernal door. Here was a chance to vent our feelings. The racket we made in the job was satisfying to both of us. One panel was split in several places. A moment later we should have had splinters flying into the hall when the door opened and the owner peeked in. One look at his face was enough to still the thoughts of the verbal abuse which was ready on my lips. The dealer, who was an oldish man, was as pale as clay, perspiring and shaking. He gasped for a statement of results and I told him we had both cobras.

That was a day — not to be forgotten!

THE RED GHOST

by *Svend Fleuron*

Svend Fleuron, now ninety and living at Oresund not far from Copenhagen, is both a poet and a naturalist. He has been called the patron saint of animals, for he has always fought on their behalf against everything that threatens their liberty and natural existence. The mastery of this Danish writer is perhaps best shown in his descriptions of forest and moorland country and his acute observation of wild life. He likes to look at the world of men from the animals' point of view and the characters in his stories are, as here, frequently both rascally and humorous.

He was only one fox in one wood, but all the game in the wood knew him. He always moved about lurking and prying, as if hatching plots. No other fox surpassed him in cunning, quickwittedness or experience. "The Red Ghost" the hunter called him, and rightly so. Turning up suddenly, he soon vanished like a ghost.

One winter when much snow had fallen, he regularly caught the scent of man on a track between the firs, a track where he used to slink. The scent led to what seemed to be a giant mushroom, deep in the wood. When, at midday, men's boots ceased to rustle around the little mushroom-shaped feeding station, all the pheasants in the wood knew their meal was ready and flocked trustingly inside.

Red, the fox, never thought of attacking them overtly. He was too experienced to hope that such a scheme would work. He had to be there before them.

When the bare trunks of the trees in the cold wood were steeped in the red light of the setting sun and when the sound of hard grains being crunched by beaks told him that the whole flock of pheasants was busy pecking up the corn, Red slid forth from the shadow of the fir-trees above the mushroom. Yellow and red, he resembled a broad ray of the wintry sun itself. No one saw the old poacher. The guests were inside and he, as usual, outside and unwelcome. The "mushroom" swayed on its rickety stalk. Then, the pheasants did not know how, there was a flash, a pungent smell, teeth in a wry face and tearing claws. The Red Ghost was among them.

Of course, he could not resort to this ruse again, but had to return to well-tried methods — lying in wait for hares behind a fence or tracking down wounded game.

One morning he was following the trail of such a wounded animal. The sleuthing was easy and swift both in the snow drifts the wind had piled up and on the dry, withered floor of the wood. Absorbed in his search, he sauntered back and forth, starting again each time he lost the trail. The tip of his nose twitched as he trotted along and the corners of his muzzle puckered up when he lifted his head to sniff the air. Then, too, his white cheeks and dirty jaw were visible as he pricked his ears and kept a keen watch on his surroundings.

The trail passed a group of small firs.

All of a sudden a bushy tail, apparently pushing something in front of it, crossed his path. The fluffed-up hair of its tail prevented him from seeing the squirrel's body and gave the animal a tinge of fiery red. Hop, hop, hop! The fox saw its legs moving gingerly and its ears twitching — until the squirrel stopped with a jerk and began scratching at a fir-cone which had fallen to the ground.

Red hated squirels. Still, the fellow would taste delicious — if one could get hold of him. The fox dropped down on his belly, ready to pounce.

Like a little monkey, the squirrel squatted down and continued nibbling at its thin fir-cone when, at last, it noticed the big robber in front of it in the snow. Alarmed, the squirrel kicked out with its hind-paws and waved its tail like a fan. Red's nose grew longer; he craned his neck, pricked his ears, arched his back and beat the snow with his white-tipped brush. The two red animals looked at each other in those white surroundings and they considered the chances they had. Quickly the "monkey" got moving and rushed skyward, up the trunk of a little fir. But the pursuit had only just seriously begun.

Below, the fox chased his quarry which boldly balanced from tree-top to tree-top while he, leaping several yards high, kept snapping at it. He penetrated into the thicket of small firs and showed up in the welter of green needles like a red flame. Once, the squirrel jumped right over his back — an insolence which maddened the great freebooter. Then the acrobat gave the fox the slip by climbing up into an old spruce where the shiny tips of his ears promptly rose above a branch. Pshaw, pshaw! The squirrel rapped the branch with his little hind-paws and puffed out his tail — pshaw! But Red behaved as if nothing had happened although he understood the abuse which his impertinent little adversary heaped on him.

He was about to resume his thoughtful investigation of the trail of the wounded animal when he discovered the sorry remains of a pheasant which the hunters had brought to grief and which hung limply in the spruce. But how to get the bird? His brush gracefully upright, he jumped with his eyes on the prey, measuring the distance. The pheasant seemed to be just within reach. Red bent his back and pushed off. No luck. He veered and jumped from the other side. He kept jumping from all possible angles. In the end he was spinning like a top, his nose and ears directed at the prey. The hole which he thus dug did not reduce the distance separating him from the pheasant.

Perhaps it's a trap, he comforted himself. And, with his mind at ease, he ambled off.

However, he could not forget the pheasant in the green branch of the spruce. It smelled so enticingly of game! And, one night soon after, when there was a full moon, he discovered the slender trunk of a beech which almost touched the spruce. The fox took a run at it. He managed to put his fore-legs across some branches of the beech. The third time he contrived at last to cling to the tree. He craned his neck backwards and stretched himself as much as he could but, alas, he failed to reach the fat morsel even though the tip of the spruce branch tickled his nose. Then he snapped at it and swung himself to the spruce. The branch jerked back, was dragged down to the ground by the weight of the fox and let go of its burden.

The incident left a deep impression on Red and enhanced his self-confidence. Whenever he met the "monkey" who was so fond of fir-cones he unconsciously established a link between the squirrel's presence and some pleasant surprise. And when, inevitably, his expectations were disappointed, the malicious tricks which the little rascal played on him infuriated him even more. Quick, vivacious and never duped — that was the squirrel. How, then, could Red avoid hating the shameless little beast which, by its actions and especially by the way it pounded on the bark with its hind-legs, made it clear that up there in the tree-tops it was superior even to an old and wily fox?

Red far excelled other foxes in experience. He was a wonderful hunter, thanks to his cunning.

He had noticed that birds, insects and all other creatures put strange trust in whatever lay sprawling on the ground, still and seemingly dead. One day, therefore, Red stretched out full length near his lair, his brush and neck long and his eyes closed. He let the flies alight on the corners of his eyes and on his muzzle. He suffered terribly, but he stuck to his purpose, acting the part of a dead fox. The crows swarmed round him, anxious to find out whether the carcass already smelled carrion-like. They still kept at a respectful distance, but he did not move. The crows grew bolder and some pecked at his back while others took a stab at his legs. But the fox became himself again only when one of the crows was right in front of his muzzle. He started up from his foxy sleep and clutched the crow so violently that his jaws crunched against each other in the bird's body. The other crows never forgot that and croaked whenever they spotted him.

One day the hostile, hot-headed croaking of the crows was heard by the hunter who was always ready for an encounter with The Red Ghost. He saw something reddish glimmering between some beech-stumps and the very tall grass of a meadow on the edge of the wood. He recognized it immediately — the brush of a fox! The hunter froze.

The fox's brush kept bobbing now this way, now that, up and down and sideways. The hunter espied a squirrel which, attracted by the phenomenon, approached inquisitively. When the squirrel had come near, the hunter saw to his great surprise that Red, who had been hiding in the grass, turned to face the animal. So, it was a trick! The fox had used his brush to lure his prey and, when Little Curiosity had come close enough, the owner of the brush suddenly lept up. But he caught no more than the squirrel's scent, and the wild chase began.

The fox was at the heels of the fugitive squirrel which threw itself into a ditch. Red followed and the chase went on in the ditch, up and down, down and up. Every moment the hunter believed that the fox would catch his prey. But he was mistaken. The squirrel reached a little birch and ran up the trunk while the fox jumped after him and got a few hairs of the squirrel's tail in his teeth. The "monkey of the north" was safe and sat in the top of the tree reviling his pursuer who, reclining on his brush and panting, stared up.

Then the hunter thought the time had come to interfere. At last, he thought as he hid behind a tree, at last I have met The Red Ghost.

He compressed his vocal cords and imitated the woeful screams of a hare. At once the greedy, artful, broad face of the fox turned toward him. Red glared at the hunter who without hesitation took aim at the wild beast. A loud report of the rifle and The Red Ghost fell over on his back. The hunter hurried to the spot, but Red was gone and the man never saw him again.

THE PLAYFUL LIONS

by Osa Johnson

When young Osa and Martin Johnson, explorers and photographic
recorders of native and animal life in Borneo, returned home to New
York, they met Carl Akeley, the great sculptor, naturalist and director of
the American Museum of Natural History. He came to dinner in their
apartment, and urged certain future plans upon Martin Johnson. Mrs. Johnson, Osa, quotes his significant admonition:

"You have a very important mission, Martin," Mr. Akeley said. "Even
more important than mine . . . I have made it my mission to perpetuate
vanishing wild animal life in bronze and by securing specimens for the
Museum. You are doing the same thing in film which is available to
millions of people all over the world." . . . He suggested British East
Africa as the best place in the world for our film studies of wild animal
life, and so this became our next goal.

In the course of the ensuing months, the Johnsons not only went to
British East Africa, but they settled there in a camp at a place they named
Lake Paradise and made a film record. The following story is from Osa
Johnson's book *I Married Adventure*.

Slowly but with gratifying results, the specimens for the Museum
groups were obtained. Martin, as always, worked steadily away at
his film record and at length we decided to go down to Nairobi
and join Carl Akeley on a *safari* into the lion country, the Serengetti.
. . . The lion, we knew, would be our next study, and this *safari* with
Carl would be valuable as a preliminary step.

Making an impressive array with the Eastman, Pomeroy and
Akeley parties, Messers. Leigh, Rockwell, Raddatz and Jansson and
all our own following and equipment, we set out toward a section
southeast of Nairobi in Tanganyika Territory. A desolate waste in
the foothills at the edge of the great plains, it is a rough, practically
waterless section and quite different from the northern country.
While not far from civilization, these foothills are isolated by natural
barriers and, at the time of our first visit at least, were considered
among the best game countries in the world.

Martin and I and the Eastman party selected a camp site sheltered
by a grotesque rock formation, while Carl Akeley and his hard-
working little group set up tents nearby.

While we were getting our camp settled, Phil Percival and Martin

reconnoitered for traces of lions and returned on the run to report a big game migration only a few miles distant.

The next morning we were out early and it was not very long before we witnessed one of the most amazing sights of our travels. Stretched far and wide as far as the eye could see were animals. It was breathtaking. There were tens of thousands of wild beasts. Those who have seen but one or two isolated animals such as ostrich, zebra, giraffe in zoos or circuses can have no conception of what it would mean to see miles and miles of unfamiliar animals. There were countless wildebeeste, Thompson's gazelle, Grant's gazelle, warthog, topi, kongoni, giraffe, hyena, ostrich, jackal. High overhead, vultures floated in wide circles on motionless wings.

We all took pictures like mad, and it wasn't until we returned to camp that night, tired and quite beside ourselves with excitement, that we realized we had not seen a single lion. This was going to be something to tease Carl Akeley about, we said... We had just finished dinner that evening, however, when Carl Akeley rushed into our camp.

"I've found them," he announced excited.

At dawn the next morning we were on our way with Carl in the lead. "I don't believe this pride has ever been disturbed," he said.

I could see that Martin was dubious; one only spoke of animals "not being disturbed" up at Lake Paradise.

We trudged for hours up the dry rocky plains, sweating and miserable. The blazing tropical sun produced heat waves that fairly frizzled us, while fine dust rose to torture our nostrils. ... We followed Carl into a shallow depression between two hills. Here he stopped and motioned us to be silent, and a lion crossed our path not ten yards away. If it was aware of us, it didn't even bother to look around. And then, to our astonishment, eleven full-grown lions emerged.

We hadn't the remotest idea what to expect. Eleven great lions not ten yards away! All I could do was hope they weren't hungry. Martin's eyes fairly popped, and Mr. Eastman went to work at once with his 16 mm Cine. This reminded my husband that he also had a camera with him and as quietly and speedily as might be, he set it up. To our amazement the tawny beasts still paid little attention, though the click of the camera seemed to tickle their ears a little and they twitched them slightly. It was I, of course, who had to grow noisily excited. Up to now they had merely turned their heads toward us and blinked lazily; several had yawned, but at the sound of my voice they faced us sharply, their muscles bulging under their shining coats. Several switched their tails and growled, and while I don't know about the others of our party, I do know that I was goose bumps from head to foot.

The lions, however, after a moment or two of consideration seemed to conclude either that we were not good food or that we just didn't matter one way or the other, so, rolling over, they stuck their feet in the air, and went fast asleep.

We were all so happy we could scarcely contain ourselves, and exchanged congratulatory grins.

My husband ground hundreds of feet of film of the lovely big cats, Mr. Eastman's camera buzzed and finally we all decided to leave, when a twelfth lion, bigger than any of the rest, meandered into the scene, eyed his sleeping companions whimsically for a few moments, then apparently decided to tease them a little. He mauled and mouthed them, every last one, until he had them all awake. The donga resounded with their growls and snarls of irritation and then, as suddenly as he had started his little game, the big fellow thought he too would like a nap and presently twelve kingly beasts lay, feet in the air, snoring blissfully. We tiptoed away . . .

We were to have made another visit to the lion valley early the next day, but when we called for Carl we found him desperately ill . . .

"Go ahead, Martin," Carl said to my husband. "Go ahead with your work. Get all the data and the pictures you can — through them better than any other way the world will come to know about animals — about lions. Sportsmen, so-called, too; I want them to know how unsportsmanlike it is to slaughter animals simply for the sake of slaughter."

He was quiet for a minute and then smiled again. "An even dozen, like so many tabby cats, fast asleep on their backs — and we only ten yards away."

BOOMER, A KANGAROO

by *Denis Clark*

Denis Clark, a rebel against the regimentation of his military schooling in England, cut away from home to go to the Far East, and there — in Ceylon, at eighteen — he became manager of a plantation. For some years he was an enthusiastic hunter. He had hair-breadth escapes in encounters with a bear, a rogue elephant, a leopard elephant, a leopard. Two years of his life he spent working with some German settlers, on a wild East African farm, where hunting game for food was a daily necessity.

Capital; but, in time, after his marriage and success as a writer, Denis Clark came to feel strongly (as his wife relates) that there were better ways to know animals than through destroying them. Where he has written of black leopards — as he has done compassionately in *Black Lightning* — of a kangaroos, as he did in *Boomer*, he has shared with his reader not only a good story, but deep knowledge of the ways of his animal characters.

Here the little "joey" who becomes the Boomer of Denis Clark's *Boomer*, is introduced:

The stretching landscape of parched grass and sparse, open groves gave small welcome to beast or to man. Yet it was here the kangaroo doe gave birth to her baby, the old boomer's son. This comfortless place was to her fair as anywhere else. Not for her the need to search for a den or some deep-hidden nest in the woods. She was spared all such worry and care, for when her young one should be born he would have his own mobile home like a gipsy or snail.

A little way off from the rest of the mob she seated herself on her broad stern close to an acacia stump. The others lay in odd postures, some at full length on their sides, hind legs outstretched or curled sideways, their hand-like forepaws restlessly scooping dust over them to drive off the pestering flies. Others lay flat on their bellies, heads on folded paws or with those paws pushed forward in pose of a *lion couchant*. No sound came from the bush but the buzz of crickets and cicadas, the faint cracks of bursting seed pods. Even the kookaburras and crows were silent through these baking afternoon hours.

Beside the acacia stump where had been one now were two, though the creature newly arrived was so small at this first appearance as to make it seem rather to belong to the insect world than to the animal. Strange indeed that a beast large as man should give

107

birth to a babe so diminutive, for in size the new-born kangaroo
was scarcely larger than the top joint of man's little finger. Yet,
though barely out of its embryo state, it was a perfect, tiny animal;
and the little slug-thing was alive, with an instinctive will of its
own, its own urgent plans for survival. After the efforts involved
in its birth,for a short while it lay at rest, exposed on the flat base
of its mother's tail which stretched forward between her hindquarters. Then with groping but purposeful movements it started
to crawl up the smooth, swelling slope of her body, pushing its way
through her hair, up and on as if in earnest search of some objective.

For nearly a half-hour it struggled, its mother the while showing
no sign she knew it was there as she reclined indolently, her back
resting against the stump. Only once when it started to stray on a
path which would quickly have led it to fall from its upward curved
platform did one of her claw-fingered hands stir as if she would
direct its passage. But unaided it resumed the trail which led on to
its haven.

That haven was a snug pouch open und ready half-way up the
mother beast's belly. When her little one found it at last it tumbled
its way headlong into its welcoming fold, eagerly seeking and finding
the ultimate thing it desired. This was a soft, tempting nipple to
which it greedily attached its small, nuzzling mouth. Nipple and

mouth locked together like socket and ball, not again to be separated until many weeks had gone by.

So the weeks and months passed as, ensconced in his furry retreat, the joey grew large and fat. Often he ventured out now, for he was more than half weaned. Very shyly at first, then more and more boldly, he slipped from his mother's warm nest to gambol or graze with other joeys of the mob. Always at an inkling of danger, a warning call from his parent, he was ready to rush helter-skelter, to tumble in head over heels, righting himself in a moment to peer cheekily from her pouch.

There were enemies in the bush, in the grass plains, in the trees. Australia has only one carnivorous four-footed animal, the red dog or dingo, but dingoes love young kangaroos, old ones too for that matter, and the mob must be always alert for their sneaking approach. Sometimes at night they would hear the uncanny dog howls and the worried creatures would sit up testing the breeze, their ears tense and erect. Besides wild dogs there were snakes which would happily swallow a young kangaroo whole for breakfast without thinking anything of it. But those were not common, and the smaller, venomous serpents would not attack except when angered.

Not all the young joey's enemies lived on the ground though. High in the sky black shapes circled with taut wings whose pinions stretched wide like great hands. Those dark-plumaged birds of prey had eyes a hundred times keener even than any black man's. In a flash when a good target offered they would rush plunging to attack. Instinct, and instinct alone, saved the young kangaroo's life the first time he made their acquaintance.

It was dawn and the mother kangaroo drank at a "billabong", a long, clear creek fringed by reeds, in a hollow among groves of golden-flowered wattle trees.

The blue doe hopped slowly down, her fur spangled with dew and the clinging tendrils of spiders, which festooned her coat like seed pearls. The air was sweet with bird song and the scent of mimosa. She and her joey sucked deep of the sweet, chilly water which was filtered and fed by some secret, underground spring. The joey sat erect, startled, as a brown shape swirled and bobbed up not far from his nose. He could see it now under the surface, swimming with its broad, webbed feet, rolling playfully, pale belly upwards. Another of its kind had joined it, and the two creatures gambolled and splashed in the billabong's shallows. Odd beasts

111

they were, with the body and fur of an otter but, instead of the blunt, cat-like head, their faces prolonged into flat, horny bills like a duck's. The platypus had her nest too in a tunnel dug deep inside the water hole's bank, but when her two eggs would be hatched she and her mate would not need to forage for their young like the kookaburras and magpies. Despite the fact that she laid eggs, she was a mammal, and like all other animals would suckle her babes at her breast. Strange freaks of nature were they, which had somehow got mixed up between bird and beast in the misty past of evolution.

Lovely and calm as the morning was, for some reason the doe was uneasy. Twice as she drank she raised herself fully erect, balancing on tip of tail and hind-toes to stare up and backward. Thirst quenched, she turned round to hop off, her joey, that lazy young rascal, at once making a dive for her pouch. While he was able to use it he did not intend to abandon so comfortable a way of travelling. Had he but known it, this was to be the last of his passenger days.

But the doe hopped on, brushing him to one side with her haunch. She was worried still. Her ears were pricked inquiringly, her nose was testing the air. Out of the hollow she climbed, the offended joey fussing and nudging against her, up the slope where the parched grass began, to rejoin the rest of her mob. They had been here a few minutes ago. Where were they now? Unaccountably they had vanished. Only a "native companion", a tall gray crane with cheeks of apoplectic red, stalked stiffly across her path, then ran a short distance with curious, mincing dance steps, flapping its wings and sailed off.

She was still staring round her, seeking the mob when the first red dog came in sight. It came rustling through the long grass, foxlike yet heavier, more to be feared than a fox. The mother kangaroo saw it, swung round and bounded away, as it seemed in a single moment. As she leapt past the joey her two short arms reached out and down, snatching his fat body up and thrusting it into her pouch. Then she was away with five dingoes fast on her heels.

They ran silent and grim, a dam and four nearly grown cubs. For the previous half-hour they had been stalking the mob, but the mob had been warned in good time by the clamour of a pair of "dollar birds", close cousins of the English jay, which had spotted the sneaking red bodies from the branch of a tall stringy-bark. The mob had dispersed as it always did when there was danger, and the dingoes had quartered back and forth confused by the interrupted, crisscrossing trails. Through the long grass and thick scrub they had not got a sight of their quarry until unexpectedly they found the kangaroo mother.

She was up and away, clearing an arm of the billabong in a long leap, bounding off through the grass, past the wattle trees, making for a wood of gums where the rough going would help her flight. The dogs followed without a sound, deadly sinister, bunching together.

In the first flurry they almost caught her. Heavy laden as she was with the dead weight of her joey, they came very near to closing with her in the open. They were spreading to head and turn her when good fortune came to her rescue. A cock emu jumped suddenly up off its nest of nine large, dark green eggs, from which, in excess of fatherly zeal, it had driven its mate. Now, so rudely interrupted in its incubatory duties, it flustered away angrily. Instinct to safe-guard its young made it run furtively for some distance, its intention

to expose itself when well away from the nest and so lure off the intruders. But the dingoes had spread in a crescent which embraced the coolabah tree at whose foot the rude nest had been made. Seeing its precious though so far inanimate family directly threatened, the emu came tearing back, running straight into one of the hunters.

Knowing no better, the cub sprang savagely to rip down the great, outraged bird. The cock emu stood six feet high, a sullen, forbidding giant with a compact body clad in a brownish-black garment which rather resembled coarse hair. Its eyes glittered devilishly, its broad beak was poised to strike and bite on the end of its long snake-like neck. In looks it bore a peculiar resemblance to its companion "aboriginal", the Australian blackfellow. It lashed viciously at the dingo with a leg armed with more deadly muscular power than the chief of all champion footballers. That kick was as fierce as a horse's, augmented by hard, polished nails. The dingo sailed cartwheeling backwards with an astonished, agonized yelp. Dazed and shaken it picked itself up to limp after the pack, which had faltered but then gone ahead. The crafty old mother-dog never strayed from the easier game, the more promising meal. But the little diversion had meant extra minutes of life to the kangaroo doe.

Panting with her heavy burden (who regarded the undulatory snatches of landscape as they went leaping across it, but otherwise gave no assistance) she reached the trees, threading them while a storm of white cockatoos swept screaming out of their branches. Here were dried gullies, thorny thickets, great logs, obstacles which slowed the dingoes' earthbound progress while she went sailing above them. If she could but reach the river she hoped that she might shake them off in the tangle of scrub on its bank, in the maze of long pools and sand beaches where scent would be lost. Downhill she tore at breakneck speed for the river's kind sanctuary.

The mother dingo saw that slaty-blue shape go bouncing and bounding before her, down out of sight, then up again like a bird or a ball. Silent and avid she twisted and turned on its trail, never heeding the scent of bandicoot, lizard or fowl which scampered or flew from her way. She hoped now to bay the kangaroo down in the river, for she knew how often when hard-pressed these creatures chose water in which to make their last stand. Three cubs ran close on her heels, the other some distance behind, making the best pace he could on but three of his legs. One shoulder blade had been cracked by the cock emu's kick.

116

Careering down that steep hillside, it seemed a miracle that the kangaroo kept her feet and her wild, flying course. The base for her leap was frequently most unfavourable, a thicket or crumbling hollow, while until the moment of arrival she never knew where she would land. True, she was able to maintain a certain guidance over her flight by means of her tail, which to some extent combined the functions of an aircraft's rudder and elevator. Without it she would have been lost. How else to correct the bias imparted to a leap between trees at an oblique angle to her intended direction? She had, too, the asset of extremely excellent landing gear, in the shape of her long and resilient hind-feet which supported the springs of her haunches. And she had all the confident balance of an expert skijumper. In the air she did not falter or topple, and when she landed, her weight was so distributed that, unshaken and steady, she was ready at once to gather herself and take off on another astonishing bound. So, without accident and the joey still safely aboard, she arrived at the coolabah trees which fringed the wide river, the old friendly avenue of emerald-starred gold and silver between long green banks.

Her anxious eyes sighted a lengthy, scrub-covered island, cut off only by a shallow, mirror-still pool out of which a kingfisher flirted, flashing upstream with a tiny, bright fish in its beak. She could go no farther. She would hide there, trusting the wild dogs would mislay her tracks in the water. Splash, splash! She started towards it, then stopped, miserable and uncertain, to change her direction completely and limp heavily along the exposed sandy beach.

The dingoes shot out of the trees, not forty yards behind her. Red beasts, they swept over the sun-caked, sparkling sand. But only three of them followed the kangaroo's trail. The mother, that cunning old hunter, kept inside the screen of tall trees, galloping hard to head off the poor, distressed prey.

She heard them and tried one final attempt for escape. With almost the last of her strength she made a jump back for the trees. By herself she would have far rather chosen the river, where still she might have lost the dogs or, at worst, have met their attack on more level terms in the water. She was no valiant old boomer to defend herself in a fierce stand-up fight to a finish. But kangaroos know how to swim and, in the river, the dingoes would not have had it all their own way, as they had it now.

But she could not take to that cool sanctuary with the joey. He could not swim yet. He would drown. There was nothing for it but to go plunging on through the trees. And among those trees, racing almost level with her, was the red shape of the dingo dam.

So far the kangaroo doe had been a good mother, but there is a limit to the sacrifices of parenthood. It was obvious that with her burden she could never get away now. She and her joey together would make meat for the fierce, silent dingoes.

Once more she jinked. On her left flank now the three cubs were closing in fast. She saw that the end was in sight and took the last desperate action which mothers of her kind take when the need demands. Speeding along at full stretch, in mid-leap her forepaws reached into her pouch, lifting the warm, furry joey and flinging him out to one side. Snatched suddenly from his retreat, he fell with a protesting grunt, but instinct asserted itself and the joey went hopping away at a tangent to his mother's trail. The dingoes might still have pursued him, an easy titbit, but the mother doe unexplainedly faltered and tumbled, compelling their greedy attention. Why on the level did she come to grief now, who had never stumbled in all that wild, headlong chase? Feeble and panting, even in her

118

own extremity, did she fall to rescue her joey, to give him a small chance of life, a few moments to make his escape while the dingoes raced up to her? Perhaps she did. Mother wild ducks sham wounded and linger at the hunter's mercy to distract him from their young. Why should a kangaroo be any less of a mother?

Perhaps, even so, she had hoped that she still might evade them, that when the dingoes had been led far off and lost she might come hopping back for her baby. She jumped up and made two more bounds, but her strength had gone now and the dingoes had drawn in too close. The red dam sprang up at her throat, throwing her off her balance. One leap she made, the wild dog swinging from her shoulder. Then she was down and the three cubs tore at her soft flanks. The fourth cub had just come in sight, limping as best he was able, inspired by the sight of the feast, when a spear whistled out of the bushes impaling his mother. One of his brothers yelped and sprang into the air as a boomerang caught it squarely between ear and neck. The other two turned round and bolted, leaving their whimpering, snapping parent behind. The late comer halted, wounded leg lifted, fear and disgust in his eyes, then he too turned and hobbled away dot and carry. From the edge of the river three blackfellows, skinny and naked, came striding towards the dead beasts.

FIREPOINT

by H. Mortimer Batten

Harry Mortimer Batten was born in 1888 in Singapore but he returned to school in England. Later he joined the Canadian Police and in Canada learnt at first hand much of the knowledge which made him such a successful and convincing writer of animal stories. He wrote unsentimentally and without unduly softening the harshness of the eternal struggle for survival waged by all animals in the wild. This story comes from *Romances of the Wild.*

One of our wise men has said that the cat is the most perfectly formed of all warm-blooded, four-footed things, and perfect indeed was Firepoint, perfect as the hissing, snarling, bristling, sinister embodiment of sin, as she came down from the Bennan Heights to make a home in Colgarth Ravine. She did not come of her own choice. Oh no! The events of recent days had somewhat precipitated matters; and that is why we see the wild cat peering into every cranny, creeping in and out of every fissure of the rocks, till at length she came to an anchorage in a round hollow among the roots of the wind-fallen pine bridging the burn. It was, indeed, an ideal nesting-place for her — save for circumstances which became evident later, and over which she had no control. The ravine was deep and narrow, and on this side of it the cliffs rose almost vertically for close upon a hundred feet, piled boulder upon boulder, each shelf overhung by a sheltering growth of ferns and mountain ash. The only way down to the windfall was afforded by these shelves, leaping from one to another, as Firepoint had done, and the only way across the burn was by that fateful fallen tree which the wild cat had appropriated.

Firepoint was perhaps wise in her hasty choice, for instinct or judgment told her that the prostrate trunk formed the chief highway to and from the wood on this side. She could crouch in her nest and watch it as she did this evening, to the misfortune of a luckless squirrel who came jerking his way across just as the last golden beams of the sunset touched the crooked limbs with fire. Later on a

120

rabbit came hopping over in the purple gloom, and he too died. Firepoint buried them both close to her nest — against a time of possible sickness.

Yes, the ravine was ideal in many respects. The noise of pounding waters served to deaden all other sounds, save those meant for a mother's hearing, and here, shut off from the four winds, screened by Nature from any lurking foe, Firepoint and her kits might have dwelt in safety the livelong summer, but that —

But wait. The circumstances which brought about the wild cat's sudden evacuation of the Bennan Heights bear but indirectly on this story, so can be given but the briefest comment. The shepherds had put their heads together, and decided they had experienced enough of wild cats. There had been an organized hunt with dogs, sulphur fumes, and shot-guns. It had cost Firepoint her home, and it had cost one of the dogs an eye. She had fled in bristling, hissing panic — down through the fir woods to the richer growth of birch, oak, and beech at the lower levels. The naked crags were her home, the purple tundra her range, but instinct, rather than fine judgment — for even a wild cat possesses precious little of the latter — had told her that the sheltered forests were the only sanctuary at this vital season.

Night passed — dawn came. Firepoint did not emerge from her nest, though all was very silent within. Without was the pounding roar of water, above which other sounds, minute, insignificant, strove to make themselves heard. The rising sun just caught the topmost branches of the mountain ash across the burn, and there, poised aloft, showing off his coat of velvet jet to his harem in the bracken below, sat a lordly blackcock, his crimson eyebrows conspicuous from afar. He uttered a strange "chortling" note, faint, yet of immense volume, and, lower still, a fieldfare made the scene melodious with his haunting song.

Suddenly the blackcock rose with a ringing "chock-churr", and in an instant the whole bracken slope was loud with beating wings. Fourteen greyhens rose at once and went hurtling down the slope, flashing and vanishing as they shot alternately through sunlight and shadow. A braggart and a bombast he may have been, yet he knew his business, for from the tufted rocks, not twenty feet away, there rose a russet figure — standing with one paw raised, its big ears a-cock, watching the departing grouse. Then the figure vanished again, was swallowed up by the landscape, and quietude fell.

There was no breath of wind, only that fragrant freshness of the newly born day, rich with the scent of budding life, and of the dew-drenched undergrowth. Nothing seemed astir, till suddenly, as though by magic, there was a flash of gold and russet by the burn — at the very point where the prostrate pine leant its gnarled extremity upon the bank. The vixen came daintily, picking her way, her eyes half-closed, her ears laid back, and as she trotted out across the bridge the dead tree quivered slightly with her weight.

"Stop!"

The order came like the bursting of a hand grenade, and from behind the breastwork of twisted roots there flashed the most awful apparition of rage and hate the subtle mind of Dame Nature could conceive.

Firepoint was there to meet the vixen — there, in the very centre of the bridge — a brindled, bristling terror, perfect in the poise of feline menace. She looked fully the size of the fox, though the latter was of the wolfish mountain breed, for her thick coat stood on end all over her. Her ears were laid back, flat upon her devilish scalp, her eyes were indescribable — phosphorescent green, save for a pinpoint of reddest fire in the centre of each one of them. There was also an impression of curved white claws — hundreds of them, and of needle fangs, inconceivably harder than diamond. A man would have stopped dead at the sight of such a thing, a woman would have fainted, a child would probably have died of fright.

Not so the vixen. She did none of these things. She just shrank back almost imperceptibly and her eyes narrowed. Then they half-closed again and her tongue lolled out. She assumed an air of absolute indifference and there was no telling from her attitude what she would do. That is always the way with foxes; that is why they seem always to do the unexpected. But she did not go back; that was the crux of the whole thing. *She did not go back!*

Like Firepoint, Vic was desperately in earnest at this season. She would have faced anything — short of man and fire. Her hunting to-night had been disappointing and she was in no mood to be trifled with. To put it plainly — she too was a mother and this bridge was on the direct route to her den, not ninety yards away. Moreover — it was her bridge. She had used it all winter and the bark was worn smooth by the passage of her paws. Anyone who tried to obstruct her here was obstructing her in her duties of motherhood.

Even so, there are some who know the ways of Reynard who will still expect her to turn back. The mothers of the wild respect each other's rights and privileges, and Reynard is at any time too wise to rush into a fight with a formidable foe. He loves the sunshine and the bright scenes of life. What he lacks in experience he knows by instinct concerning wild cats, and he likes to make sure of his eyes for another day.

Vic patiently waited for Firepoint to remove herself, but there was no such intention in the mind of the feline. Vic quietly lay down and waited; then Firepoint set up a caterwaul, beginning with a high F sharp, wavering, tailing off, growing in volume, sinking to a rumbling bass, then ending spasmodically with a fine display of Chinese crackers, whizz-bangs, and bursting motor-tyres. The latter were accompanied by terrific forepaw thumps on the bark, which set the chips flying, but Vic calmly scratched her ear with her hind paw.

What happened next was too meteoric and swift for human eye to follow. The vixen charged straight at the feline. Firepoint timed things to a nicety — so far as one can time meteoric effects. She shot straight into the air and by all the laws of gravity she should have been the exact height of the vixen's back, descending rapidly, as the vixen passed below.

But the vixen did not pass below. She knew something about felines. That dash of hers was all a huge bluff, for a foot from the cat she stopped dead, and up went her head with an odd, sidelong

shake. There was a "chop-click" of iron teeth, and the would-be Horatius, spinning wildly in mid-air, vanished over the edge into the smother of foam.

Vic, with ears a-cock, watched her going. The burn was swollen by recent rains, and was descending a one-in-five gradient. The pale sunlight now penetrated the ravine. A dipper flew by screaming, horrified at what had happened, and Firepoint, sucked into the central race, went down and over.

Blood was dripping from Vic's nose, but now she trotted unconcernedly on. Encircling the roots she stopped dead, for the faintest of faint whimperings reached her ears. The hair on her shoulder-blades stood on end, she glanced half-timidly down the ravine, then she began to dig. She dug out Firepoint's kits, chopped them one by one, then defiled them where they lay — the sign of her uttermost contempt.

Not vixen spite alone was at the root of these unpardonable doings, for, between the foxes and the wild cats of the hills there exists a feud — older than any feudal bitterness of man. In the world of men time changes all things; the peoples of the nations rise and slay each other and in a century — yes, less — the sons of victor and vanquished are fighting side by side. In the wild nothing changes; there is no unity of purpose to draw old foes together. The feuds are world-old, bloody, unending feuds, backed by inherited hate, immutable as time itself. The enemies may dwell in peace door by door for a decade or so, but should chance one day throw one upon the mercy of the other, there is no mercy shown and none expected. Armed neutrality is common order, death is the penalty for weakness, and never a stone is left unturned to perfect history's repetition.

Vic had taken the most dreadful vengeance in all the wild; she had exacted her indemnity to the last drain of blood, and now she hurried away from the place as though fearful of being seen, and went to her own cubs. She remained with them all day, listening constantly, and at night she carried them one by one to quite a distant den, putting running water between them and the place where lived the wild cat.

Ten minutes after her defeat, Firepoint came gliding back towards her lair. Her long coat, dripping water, clung to the sinuous contour of her frame. She gurgled and coughed, as she leapt from rock to rock, and like a shadow of her former self she sought her den.

Vic! Vic! What have you done? Is there no law in all the woods

that you respect — no law save the law of self-survival and the plenteous nursing of your cubs? See, the ringdove nests beside the sparrow-hawk, but her little ones thrive secure! A mother cony rears her young at the foot of the peregrine's crag, but these children of the wild dispute not each other's right to live and multiply, for there is a law more binding than the only law you choose to keep. And, as sure as night follows day, as sure as autumn brings her golden leaves and floating gossamer, that justice will avenge the breach of the law you set at naught.

As for this mother, this poor, broken-hearted woodland mother, the last of her kind on all the Bennan Range, she crouched by that defiled and trampled heap in the golden morning light. All the fight was gone out of her now. She scraped the dead leaves over them and went away. She seemed to regard what had happened as inevitable under the circumstances. She had no thought of immediate vengeance, only — there remained the feud. Not only inherited enmity now, but an all-absorbing personal hatred, backed with undying bitterness by a sense of irredeemable wrong. It touched the wild cat's brain with fingers of fire, it drew its burning tentacles down her spine so that she quivered and writhed beneath its touch. Sooner or later Firepoint and her foe would meet; sooner or later, in the face of the great justice of the wild, they would be weighed in the balance together.

Many times that summer Vic found the scent of the feline perilously near her cubs, many times she moved them from place to place, climbing higher up the mountainside to the lands of drifting mist, where the firs were draped and bearded with lichen, but in time she came to know what Eugene Aram knew. She grew lean and gaunt, anxious eyed with unending watchfulness, while her pretty little ones, with no knowledge of the haunting dread they caused, showed each day a more perilous desire to wander off. Once Vic found the dreaded scent at her very threshold, and frenzied with fear and rage she hunted back and forth — running the scent eventually to the foot of a twisted pine. And there, just beyond her reach, stood Firepoint, eyes gleaming, back arched. Dead to all sense of pain Vic leapt and leapt again, failing each time by an inch or so, and each time Firepoint's claws ripped and gashed her face till she was daubed and dripping, Vic gave it up and again moved her cubs. Her coat had lost its lustre now; she was lean and hollow as a February wolf.

Then one night the vixen, prowling through the phosphorescent gloom of the tundra heights, saw Firepoint stealing out across the tablelands. The fox back-tracked quietly to the white-walled homestead on the southern side, and yapped a mocking "gurr-yap" through the gates. Out dashed two sturdy sheepdogs, sons of another feud, skilled in hunting together, versed in the ways of the wiry mountain fox. Vic knew their ways, too, and led them out across the tundra. She could trick them at any time she chose, as she had tricked them a dozen times before, but now, straight and true with the dogs behind, Vic was running a scent. Out across the tablelands it led them — off and away towards the giddy summit of the Eagles' Brow. It was Firepoint's scent she was running.

The big cat heard the sounds of death behind and cast around for a place of sanctuary. There was nothing near; the nearest trees were down across the bluff, the chaos of boulders, where once she had her den, was in the direction of her foes. Straight ahead was the giddy drop through space at the Eagles' Brow, and so, being a cat, Firepoint crouched, watching with fiendish intentness, trusting the heather to hide her.

On came Vic, loping easily — ten yards, eight yards, five, then she leapt aside, breaking her own line of scent, and leaving the bristling Firepoint dead in the pathway of her pursuers.

On — swiftly now, to the very edge of Eagles' Brow, sped the

vixen. At her feet, four hundred feet below, spread the valley, indescribably peaceful under the stars, beautiful as a sleeping child. Lightly Vic leapt — to her fate it would seem, yet she had been here before. Ten feet down was a narrow shelf, and on it she landed, lightly as a thistle seed, crouching on the scanty carpet of ling till the coast should be clear, when, by perilous ways, she could gain a rugged fissure and remount to the brow.

Swiftly pursued the dogs, till suddenly there rose from the blue expanse ahead a rumbling growl, and something barred the way. There she stood, broadside on, blotched and bristling, one paw raised — the indomitable fighter ready for action, two points of fire set in those orbs of phosphorescent green. A flash of summer lightning showed her up — showed the seamed and fissured heavens, packed with floating gossamer and angry red-ribbed clouds, till cloud and distant summit united in the coming storm.

The dogs overshot, hung back, and rallied. They were brave dogs, schooled through remorseless winters, sons of toil, inheritors of their master's feud. A silent signal passed between them and they closed.

Firepoint recoiled, for there was no meeting that deadly impact. She rose and ricochetted backwards, sending the ling tips flying from her whirling paws. The dogs were met by a cyclone, momentarily blinded, and back, back, crouched Firepoint, to the very verge of the cliff.

She was beaten and she knew it. To close meant death, yet there was no evading two of them out here in the ghastly open. Some may say she fell foul of feline panic, but I choose to think that proper understanding was here, and between two open doors she took her choice.

Death by the things she knew, up yonder, close to the clouds — death by her native crags on the dizzy heights she loved, or death with blood and thunder by those she hated and despised? Back to the very edge, still bristling, still defiant — still glorious as a creature of destruction, designed to murder and to rend, Firepoint rose at length with an awful scream of hate, then bounded lightly into space.

Ten feet below Firepoint and Vic stood face to face — at last! They looked into each other's eyes for one tense and awful instant, and each read plainly what was written there. Glowering, watchful, fully prepared, Firepoint flattened down, and Vic, at the dead end of the shelf, awaited her.

From overhead there came a roar, shaking the very mountain-side, filling the crags with rumbling voices. It was the voice of the Thunder King, omnipotent, incomprehensible, and to them it came as the signal. They approached silently, each with lowered head, and — closed. The dogs looked down, then hung back timorously. It may have been grand, it may have been inevitable, but it was horrifying. One ghostly scream rang from the dingy depths below, echoing, re-echoing from a thousand crags and crannies, as down through giddy space fell Vic and Firepoint, locked in the deathly grapple of a feud death cannot kill.

THE BATTLE OF THE FANGS

by Jack London

When he was fourteen, Jack London left school and set out to find adventure. He went to sea, lived as a tramp and tried his luck in the Klondike gold rush before writing the first of his fifty books which were to make him world famous. This episode comes from *White Fang* which was first published in 1906.

They ran many miles that day. They ran through the night. And the next day found them still running. They were running over the surface of a world frozen and dead. No life stirred. They alone moved through the vast inertness. They alone were alive, and they sought for other things that were alive in order that they might devour them and continue to live.

They crossed low divides and ranged a dozen small streams in a lower-lying country before their quest was rewarded. Then they came upon moose. It was a big bull they first found. Here was meat and life, and it was guarded by no mysterious fires nor flung missiles of flame. Splay hoofs and palmated antlers they knew, and they flung their customary patience and caution to the wind. It was a brief fight and fierce. The big bull was beset on every side. He ripped them open or split their skulls with shrewdly driven blows of his great hoofs. He crushed them and broke them on his large horns. He stamped them into the snow under him in the wallowing struggle. But he was foredoomed, and he went down with the she-wolf tearing savagely at his throat, and with other teeth fixed everywhere upon him, devouring him alive, before ever his last struggles ceased or his last damage had been wrought.

There was food in plenty. The bull weighed over eight hundred pounds — fully twenty pounds of meat per mouth for the forty-odd wolves of the pack. But if they could fast prodigiously, they could feed prodigiously, and soon a few scattered bones were all that remained of the splendid live brute that had faced the pack a few hours before.

There was now much resting and sleeping. With full stomachs, bickering and quarreling began among the younger males, and this continued through the few days that followed before the breaking-up of the pack. The famine was over. The wolves were now in the country of game, and though they still hunted in pack, they hunted more cautiously, cutting out heavy cows or crippled old bulls from the small moose-herds they ran across.

There came a day, in this land of plenty, when the wolf-pack split in half and went in different directions. The she-wolf, the young leader on her left, and the one-eyed elder on her right, led their half of the pack down to the Mackenzie River and across into the lake country to the east. Each day this remnant of the pack dwindled. Two by two, male and female, the wolves were deserting. Occasionally a solitary male was driven out by the sharp teeth of his rivals. In the end there remained only four: the she-wolf, the young leader, the one-eyed one, and the ambitious three-year-old.

The she-wolf had by now developed a ferocious temper. Her three suitors all bore the marks of her teeth. Yet they never replied in

kind, never defended themselves against her. They turned their shoulders to her most savage slashes, and with wagging tails and mincing steps strove to placate her wrath. But if they were all mildness toward her, they were all fierceness toward one another. The three-year-old grew too ambitious in his fierceness. He caught the one-eyed elder on his blind side and ripped his ear into ribbons. Though the grizzled old fellow could see only on one side, against the youth and vigor of the other he brought into play the wisdom of long years of experience. His lost eye and his scarred muzzle bore evidence to the nature of his experience. He had survived too many battles to be in doubt for a moment about what to do.

The battle began fairly, but it did not end fairly. There was no telling what the outcome would have been, for the third wolf joined the elder, and together, old leader and young leader, they attacked the ambitious three-year-old and proceeded to destroy him. He was beset on either side by the merciless fangs of his erstwhile comrades. Forgotten were the days they had hunted together, the game they had pulled down, the famine they had suffered. That business was a thing of the past. The business of love was at hand — ever a sterner and crueler business than that of food-getting.

And in the meanwhile, the she-wolf, the cause of it all, sat down contentedly on her haunches and watched. She was even pleased. This was her day, — and it came not often, — when manes bristled, and fang smote fang or ripped and tore the yielding flesh, all for the possession of her.

And in the business of love the three-year-old who had made this his first adventure upon it, yielded up his life. On either side of his body stood his two rivals. They were gazing at the she-wolf, who sat smiling in the snow. But the elder leader was wise, very wise, in love even as in battle. The younger leader turned his head to lick a wound on his shoulder. The curve of his neck was turned toward his rival. With his one eye the elder saw the opportunity. He darted in low and closed with his fang. It was a long, ripping slash, and deep as well. His teeth, in passing, burst the wall of the great vein of the throat. Then he leaped clear.

The young leader snarled terribly, but his snarl broke midmost into a tickling cough. Bleeding and coughing, already stricken, he sprang at the elder and fought while life faded from him, his legs going weak beneath him, the light of day dulling on his eyes, his blows and springs falling shorter and shorter.

134

And all the while the she-wolf sat on her haunches and smiled. She was made glad in vague ways by the battle, for this was the love-making of the Wild, the sex-tragedy of the natural world that was tragedy only to those that died. To those that survived it was not tragedy, but realization and achievement.

When the young leader lay in the snow and moved no more, One Eye stalked over to the she-wolf. His carriage was one of mingled triumph and caution. He was plainly expectant of a rebuff, and he was just as plainly surprised when her teeth did not flash out at him in anger. For the first time she met him with a kindly manner. She sniffed noses with him, and even condescended to leap about and frisk and play with him in quite puppyish fashion. And he, for all his gray years and sage experience, behaved quite as puppyishly and even a little more foolishly.

Forgotten already were the vanquished rivals and the love-tale red-written on the snow. Forgotten, save once, when old One Eye stopped for a moment to lick his stiffening wounds. Then it was that his lips half writhed into a snarl, and the hair of his neck and shoulders involuntarily bristled, while he half crouched for a spring, his claws spasmodically clutching into the snow-surface for firmer footing. But it was all forgotten the next moment, as he sprang after the she-wolf, who was coyly leading him a chase through the woods.

THE STORY OF A RED DEER

by J. W. Fortescue

The Hon. Sir John Fortescue was a country gentleman whose family had long lived on Exmoor in Devonshire. He was Librarian of Windsor Castle and a military historian.

He tells us himself how in 1897 Hugh Fortescue, a young relative of nine, asked him to write him a book and he was worried "for of making of many books there is no end, and of making of good books but small beginning" however "if men would write books to be read of the young, they must write them, not after particular study, but from the fulness and the overflowing of their knowledge of such things as they have dwelt withal, and have felt and loved beyond all others." And so he wrote of the countryside in which he had grown up, whose animals he knew intimately, and the resulting book is indeed a classic of its kind.

Although Exmoor is now a very popular holiday area the red deer still live the life described here.

The grass of the forest turned fast from green to yellow, the blossom faded off the heather, and the leaves of the woods turned to gold and to russet and to brown, and fluttered down to the kind earth which had raised them up in the spring. The nights too grew colder and colder; but the Hind and Calf did not mind that, for their coats only grew the thicker and warmer to protect them. But what was far more terrible was the hideous roaring that continued all night long in all quarters of the moor. It was some days before the Calf found out what it was, for his mother seemed always dreadfully frightened unless he were well hidden away. But once when she had left him for a short time snugly tucked away on a combe's side, he saw a great Stag come down the combe driving a little herd of half a dozen Hinds before him. The Calf was astonished at the sight of him, for the Stag was quite different now from any that he had seen in the summer. The glossy coat was gone, and the great round body was lean, ragged, and tucked up, and stained with half-dried mud. His neck again was twice its usual size and looked still bigger under its great shaggy mane; and his face was not noble and calm, but fierce and restless and furrowed by two deep dark lines, so that altogether he was a most disreputable-looking old fellow.

Presently he stopped at a little boggy spot by the water's side; and there he reared up, and plunging his great antlers into the ground he

tore it up, and sent the black mire flying over his head. Then he threw himself down into the bog and rolled in it and wallowed in it, churning it up with horn and hoof, like a thing possessed. At last he got up, all dripping and black, and stretching out his great neck, till the hair of his mane hung straight and lank with the black drops running from it, he roared and roared again with a voice so terrible and unearthly that the Calf in his hiding-place shook with fright. And no wonder, for I think that even you will be startled the first time that you hear a big Stag belling.

Very soon an answering roar came from a distance, and another Stag, as thin and fierce-looking as the first, but not quite so big, came belling up the combe. And the great Stag left the Hinds and went forward to meet him, looking very stately and grand. For he walked on tip-toe, loftily and slowly, with his head thrown back, and his chin high in air, while his eyes rolled with rage, and his breath spurted forward in jets of steam through the cold, damp air, as he snorted defiance. Then presently both Stags dropped their heads and made for each other; and they fought with locked horns,

shoving and straining and struggling, backward and forward and round and round, till the smaller Stag could fight no longer but turned and fled limping away, with the blood flowing from a deep thrust in his flank. Then the great Stag threw up his head and belled again with triumph, and huddling the Hinds together once more, he drove them on before him.

For three weeks and more this roaring and fighting continued; for Deer, you must know, put all the quarrelling of the year into a single month; which sounds like a curious arrangement, but may after all be better than that of certain other creatures, which fight the whole year round.

So the Calf passed on with his mother, away from the yellow grass of the forest to the brown heather of Dunkery. And there the heath was full of great stones, unlike any ground that he had ever travelled over before, so that he had to be careful at first how he trod. But he soon found that it was easy enough for him after he had gone a little distance; and his mother led him slowly so that he should have time to learn his way. So on they went to the very top of the ridge, and there where the heather and grass grow tuft by tuft among the brown turf-pits, in the heart of the bog, they found a herd of Deer. Such a number of them there were as he had never dreamed of. Great Stags, with three and four on top, like those that he had seen fighting, were lying down, four and five together, in perfect peace, and younger Stags with lighter heads and fewer points, and Two-year-olds, proud as Punch of their first brow-antlers, and Prickets, even prouder of their first spires than the Two-year-olds, and a score or more of Hinds, nearly all of them with Calves at foot; and standing sentry over all was old Aunt Yeld.

They went, and found Ruddy and her Calf and lay down by them, for you may be sure that mothers and Calves had a great deal to say to each other. But as the evening began to close they heard a faint, low, continuous hum from the westward, and all the hinds with one accord left the bog, and went down into a deep, snug, sheltered combe, clothed thick with dwarf oak-coppice, while the stags went to their own chosen hiding-places. Soon the hum grew louder and louder, and presently the rain began to fall in heavy drops, as the little Salmon had foretold (though how they could foretell it, I know no more than you); and then the hum changed to a roar as the Westerly Gale came up in all his might and swept across the moor. And presently an old Dog-Fox came in and shook himself and lay down not far from them on one side, and a Hare came in and crouched close to them on the other, and little birds driven from their own roosting-places flew trembling into the branches above them; but not one dared to speak except in a whisper, and then only to say, "What a terrible night!" For all night long the gale roared furiously over their heads and the rain and scud flew screaming before it; and once they heard something whistle over their heads, crying wildly in a voice not unlike a sea-gull's, "Mercy, mercy, mercy!" Then the little stream below them in the combe began to swell and pour down fuller and fuller; and all round the hill a score of other little streams swelled likewise, and came tearing

141

down the hill, adding their roar to the roar of the gale; so you may be sure that the Salmon had a fine flood to carry them down to the sea.

When the Deer moved out in the morning they found the rain and wind raging as furiously as ever, and the air full of salt from the spray of the sea; and a few hundred yards to leeward of the combe they came upon a little sooty Sea-bird, quite a stranger to them, lying gasping on the ground. The poor little fellow could only say, "Mercy, mercy, where is the sea, where is the sea? Where are my brother Petrels?" Then he flapped one little wing feebly, for the other had been dashed by the gale against a branch and broken, and gasped once more and lay quite still; nor, though the deer gazed at him for long, did he ever speak or move again. So when they had fed, the deer moved back to the shelter of the combe and lay down there once more; and as the morning grew the rain ceased, though the wind blew nearly as hard as ever. But it was still a good hour before noon when the Hare suddenly jumped up and stole out of the combe. A minute after her the Fox stood up, listened for a moment, and stole out likewise, and almost directly after him the deer all sprang to their feet; for they heard the deep note of the hounds and saw their white bodies dashing into the combe full of eagerness and fire. And if any one tells you that it is incredible that Deer, Fox, and Hare should all be lying together as I have said, you may tell him from me that I saw them with my own eyes leave the combe one after another by the same path, on just such a wild morning as I have described.

The deer moved quickly on to the hill and began to run away together; but presently Aunt Yeld, and Ruddy and her Calf, and our Hind and her Calf separated from the rest, and went away at a steady pace, for, as old Aunt Yeld said, "No hound can travel fast over Dunkery stones." And, indeed, so fond was the old lady of these stones that, when she got to the edge of them, she turned back over them again and took Ruddy with her. But our Hind and her Calf moved away a mile or two towards the forest, and finding no hounds in chase of them stopped and rested.

But after half an hour or more Aunt Yeld came galloping up to them alone, very anxious though not the least tired, and said, "I can't shake them off. Come along quick!" Then they found that the hounds were hard at their heels, and away they went, in the teeth of the gale, at their best pace. And the Calf kept up bravely, for he was growing strong, but they were pressed so hard that presently Aunt Yeld left them and turned off by herself. Then by bad luck some of the hounds forsook her line for that of his mother and himself, and drove them so fast that for the first time in their lives they were obliged to part company, and he was left quite alone. So on he ran by himself till he came to a familiar little peat-stream, which was boiling down over the stones like a torrent of brown ale; and in he jumped and ran down, splashing himself all over. Before he had gone down fifty yards he felt so much refreshed that he quite plucked up heart; so he followed the water till it joined a far bigger stream, crossed the larger stream, climbed up almost to the top of the opposite side of the combe, and lay down.

And when he had lain there for more than an hour he saw Aunt Yeld coming down to the water two or three hundred yards above the place where he lay, with her neck bowed and her grey body black with sweat, looking piteously tired and weak. She jumped straight into the flooded water and came plunging down; and only a few minutes behind her came the hounds. The moment that they reached the water some of them leaped in and swam to the other side, and they came bounding down both banks, searching diligently as they ran. Then he saw Aunt Yeld stop in a deep pool, and sink her whole body under the water, leaving nothing but her head above it. She had chosen her place cunningly, where the bank was

hollowed out and the water was overhung by a little thorn bush that almost hid her head from view. And he watched the hounds try down and down; and he now saw that two horsemen were coming down the combe's side after them, the men bending low over their saddles, hardly able to face the gale, and the horses with staring eyes and heaving flanks, almost as much distressed as Aunt Yeld herself. The men seemed to be encouraging the hounds, though in the howling of the wind he could hear nothing.

But the pack tried down and down by themselves, till at last they came to the place where Aunt Yeld was lying; and there two of them stopped as if puzzled; but she only sank her head a little deeper in the water and lay as still as death, with her ears pressed back tight upon her neck. Then at last the hounds passed on, though they were loth to leave the spot, and followed the bank down below her. But presently the Calf became aware, to his terror, that some of them were pausing at the place where he himself had left the water, and, what was more, were unwilling to leave it. And then a great black and tan hound carried the line very, very slowly a few yards away from the bank up the side of the combe, and said "Ough!" and the hounds on the opposite side of the stream no sooner heard him than they jumped in and swam across to him; so that in half a minute every one of them was working slowly up towards his hiding-place. He was so much terrified that he hardly knew whether to lie still or to fly; but presently the black and tan hound said "Ough!" once more with such a full, deep, awful note that he could stand it no longer, but jumped up at once and bounded away over the hill.

And then every hound threw up his head and yelled in a way which brought his heart into his mouth, but he was soon out of their view over the crest of the hill, and turning round set his head backward for Dunkery. And as he went he saw the horsemen come struggling up the hill, trying to call the hounds off, but unable to catch them. But he soon felt that he had not the strength to carry him to Dunkery, so he swung round again with the gale in his face, and then by great good luck he caught the wind of other deer, and running on found that it was Ruddy and her Calf.

By the time that he had joined them the men had stopped the hounds, and were taking them back to try down the water again after Aunt Yeld. But you may be sure that Aunt Yeld had not waited for them. On the contrary, she had made the best of her time, for

she had run up the big water again, turned from it up a smaller stream, and having run up that, was lying down in the fervent hope that she was safe.

And safe she was; for as luck would have it the wind backed to the south-east, and began blowing harder than ever, with torrents of rain, so that after another hour the Calf saw horsemen and hounds travelling slowly and wearily home, as drenched and draggled and miserable as a deer could wish to see them. And a little later his mother came and found him, and though she too was terribly tired, she cared nothing about herself in the joy of seeing him. Then after a time Aunt Yeld came up too and joined them, and quite forgetting that it was not at all like a stag to be soft-hearted, she came up to him and fondled him, and said, "My brave little fellow, you have saved my life to-day." So they made their way to the nearest shelter and curled up together to keep each other warm, banishing all thought of the day's adventures in their joy that they were safe.

MOSTLY MONKEYS

by Gerald Durrell

Since 1946, Gerald Durrell has been writing amusingly of his serious work as a zoologist. He went on his first animal-collecting expedition to the British Cameroons in 1947-48, and since he has been, not only back to Africa, but to South America as well. Each trip has yielded a delightful book. From *The Overloaded Ark* come these observations of monkeys made in West Africa.

We moved off towards the place Elias indicated, drifting as silently as possible through the undergrowth. I remembered suddenly that I had my field-glasses with me, and cursing myself for a fool, I unslung them and trained them on the tree-tops. I gazed up at the shimmering ocean of leaves without success, feeling unreasonably irritated that both my hunters could obviously see and hear the monkeys, while I, even with my field-glasses, could not see a living thing. Then, suddenly, out of a mass of leaves along a great black branch, trouped a delightful procession. The first monkey was an old male, his tail crooked over his back, peering from side to side as he walked out along the branch. He was coal black, with the tips of the fur on his back tinged with green, so that he had a speckled appearance. His chest was white, and on his little black face the area on and around his nose was white also, a large heart-shaped patch as glistening white as a snowball. The hair on his head was long, and stood up straight, so that he looked not unlike a golliwog stalking disdainfully through the branches. Close on his heels came his two wives, both smaller than he, and both very timid, for they had young. The first carried a minute replica of herself slung at her breast. He was as small as a newly-born kitten, and he hung under his mother's body, his long arms wrapped round her and his small hands clasping tight to the fur on her back. The other baby was older and walked cautiously behind his mother, peering fearfully down at the great drop below him, and uttering a plaintive cheeping cry. I was captivated by these babies, and as I watched them I made up my mind that I would get hold of some baby Putty-nose Guenon if I had to spend the rest of my life at it.

146

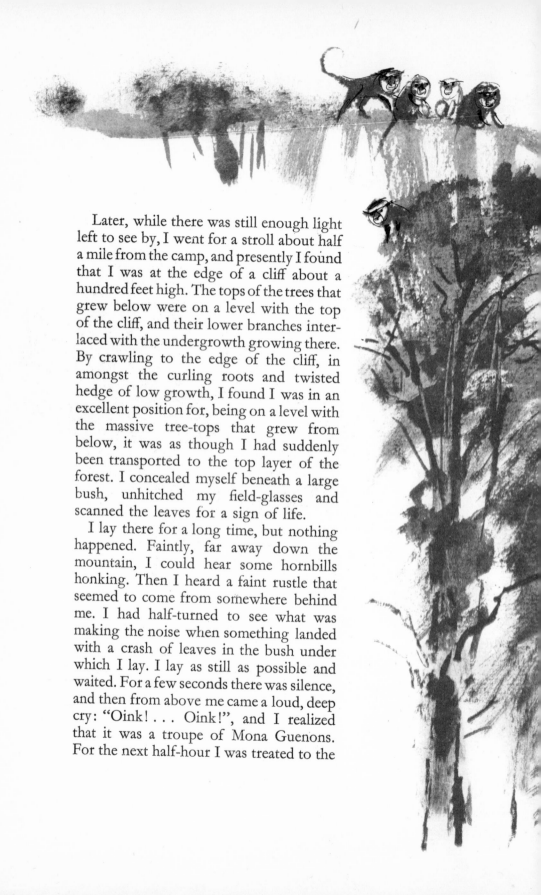

Later, while there was still enough light left to see by, I went for a stroll about half a mile from the camp, and presently I found that I was at the edge of a cliff about a hundred feet high. The tops of the trees that grew below were on a level with the top of the cliff, and their lower branches interlaced with the undergrowth growing there. By crawling to the edge of the cliff, in amongst the curling roots and twisted hedge of low growth, I found I was in an excellent position for, being on a level with the massive tree-tops that grew from below, it was as though I had suddenly been transported to the top layer of the forest. I concealed myself beneath a large bush, unhitched my field-glasses and scanned the leaves for a sign of life.

I lay there for a long time, but nothing happened. Faintly, far away down the mountain, I could hear some hornbills honking. Then I heard a faint rustle that seemed to come from somewhere behind me. I had half-turned to see what was making the noise when something landed with a crash of leaves in the bush under which I lay. I lay as still as possible and waited. For a few seconds there was silence, and then from above me came a loud, deep cry: "Oink! . . . Oink!", and I realized that it was a troupe of Mona Guenons. For the next half-hour I was treated to the

most delightful close-up of monkey life that
anyone could wish for.

The monkey in the tree above me was
presumably the leader, for he was a male of
huge proportions. Having surveyed the
forest below the cliff and seen no danger,
he had uttered his "all clear" cry to the rest
of the troupe, and then he leapt from his
bush above me and plummeted downwards
like a stone over the edge of the cliff, hands
and legs outstretched, to land among the
top branches of a tree-top just opposite to
where I was lying. He disappeared among
the leaves for a few seconds, and then
reappeared walking along a branch. When
he reached a comfortable fork he seated
himself, looked about him, and uttered a
few deep grunts.

Immediately the bush above me swayed
and shook as another monkey landed in it,
and almost in the same movement leapt
off again to drop down over the cliff into
the tree-top where the old male was waiting.
Their progression was very orderly: as one
landed in the tree below another would
arrive in the bush above me. I counted thirty
adults as they jumped, and many of the
females had young clinging to their bodies.
I could hear these babies giving shrill
squeaks, either of fear or delight, as their
parents hurtled downwards. When the
whole troupe was installed in the tree they

spread out and started to feed on a small black fruit that was growing
there. They walked along the branches, plucking the fruit and
stuffing it into their mouths, continuously glancing around them
in the quick nervous way that all monkeys have. Some of the bigger
babies had now unhooked themselves from their mother's fur and
followed them through the trees uttering their plaintive cries of
"Weeek! . . . Weeek!" in shrill quavering voices. The adults
exchanged comments in deep grunts. I saw no fights break out;
occasionally a particularly fine fruit would be snatched by one
monkey from the paws of a smaller individual, but beyond a yarring
grunt of indignation from the victim, nothing happened to disturb
their peaceful feeding.

Suddenly there was a great harsh swishing of wind and a series
of wild honking cries as two hornbills flew up from the forest
below, and with the air of drunken imbecility common to their
kind crashed to rest among the branches, in the noisy unbalanced
way that is the hornbill's idea of a perfect landing. They clung to
the branches, blinking delightedly at the Monas from under the
great swollen casques that ornamented their heads, like elongated
balloons. Then they hopped crabwise along the branches and plucked
the black fruit with the tips of their beaks most delicately. Then
they would throw back their heads and toss the fruit down their

throats. After each gulp they would squat and stare roguishly at the monkeys from their great black eyes, fluttering their heavy eyelashes. The Monas ignored these tattered clowns with their Cyrano de Bergerac profiles, and continued to feed quietly. They were used to hornbills, for what the vulture is to the lion, the hornbill is to the monkeys in the Cameroons. Whenever there is a troupe of monkeys feeding, there, sooner or later, you will find some hornbills, giving the whole position away with their loud honking and the swish of their wings, which can be heard a mile away. How the monkeys must have hated the company of these great birds, and yet they had to suffer it.

Presently the hornbills flew off with a great thrashing of wings, and soon after the leader of the Monas decided that it was time they were moving. He grunted a few times, and the mothers clasped their young to their bellies, and then they leapt, one by one, down into the foliage below, and were swallowed up in a sea of leaves. For some little time I could hear their progress through the forest below, the surging crash of leaves as they jumped from tree to tree, sounding like slow heavy breakers on a rocky shore. When I could no longer hear them I rose from my hiding-place, cramped and stiff, picked the twigs and the ants from my person, and blundered my way back to camp through the darkening forest.

THE ELEPHANTS' DANCE

by Rudyard Kipling

Better than any writer before him, Rudyard Kipling knew how to conjure up the sights and sounds of India. All the world has felt his magic in *The Jungle Book* (1895) — how the valiant little mongoose, Rikki-Tikki-Tavi, meets and taunts his mortal enemy the cobra, for example.

Equally exciting and equally to be remembered, loved, and re-read, is another, "Toomai of the Elephants", the tale of Little Toomai, who longed to see what few men see: the elephants' dance. In fact Kipling was wrong about the purpose of the "Dance Hall" he describes: it is really the maternity ward of a herd of wild elephants and it is interesting to read of the preparation of just such a place in the first story in this book, "The Presumptuous Tiger".

At last the elephants began to lie down one after another, as is their custom, till only Kala Nag at the right of the line was left standing up; and he rocked slowly from side to side, his ears put forward to listen to the night wind as it blew very slowly across the hills. The air was full of all the night noises that, taken together, make one big silence — the click of one bamboo-stem against the other, the rustle of something alive in the undergrowth, the scratch and squawk of a half-waked bird (birds are awake in the night much more often than we imagine), and the fall of water ever so far away.

Little Toomai slept for some time, and when he waked it was brilliant moonlight, and Kala Nag was still standing up with his ears cocked. Little Toomai turned, rustling in the fodder, and watched the curve of his big back against half the stars in heaven, and while he watched he heard, so far away that it sounded no more than a pinhole of noise pricked through the stillness, the "hoot-toot" of a wild elephant. All the elephants in the lines jumped up as if they had been shot, and their grunts at last waked the sleeping mahouts, and they came out and drove in the picket-pegs with big mallets, and tightened this rope and knotted that till all was quiet.

One new elephant had nearly grubbed up his picket, and Big Toomai took off Kala Nag's leg-chain and shackled that elephant fore-foot to hind-foot, but slipped a loop of grass-string round Kala Nag's leg, and told him to remember that he was tied fast. He knew that he and his father and his grandfather had done the very same

thing hundreds of times before. Kala Nag did not answer to the order by gurgling, as he usually did. He stood still, looking out across the moonlight, his head a little raised and his ears spread like fans, up to the great folds of the Garo hills.

"Look to him if he grows restless in the night," said Big Toomai to Little Toomai, and he went into the hut and slept. Little Toomai was just going to sleep, too, when he heard the coir string snap with a little "tang", and Kala Nag rolled out of his pickets as slowly and as silently as a cloud rolls out of the mouth of a valley. Little Toomai pattered after him, barefooted, down the road in the moonlight, calling under his breath, "Kala Nag! Kala Nag! Take me with you, O Kala Nag!" The elephant turned without a sound, took three strides back to the boy in the moonlight, put down his trunk, swung him up to his neck, and almost before Little Toomai had settled his knees slipped into the forest.

There was one blast of furious trumpeting from the lines, and then the silence shut down on everything, and Kala Nag began to move. Sometimes a tuft of high grass washed along his sides as a wave washes along the sides of a ship, and sometimes a cluster of wild-pepper vines would scrape along his back, or a bamboo would creak where his shoulder touched it; but between those times he moved absolutely without any sound, drifting through the thick Garo forest as though it had been smoke. He was going uphill, but though Little Toomai watched the stars in the rifts of the trees, he could not tell in what direction. Then Kala Nag reached the crest of the ascent and stopped for a minute, and Little Toomai could see the tops of the trees lying all speckled and furry under the moonlight for miles and miles, and the blue-white mist over the river in the hollow.

Toomai leaned forward and looked, and he felt that the forest was awake below him — awake and alive and crowded. A big brown fruit-eating bat brushed past his ear; a porcupine's quills rattled in the thicket; and in the darkness between the tree-stems he heard a hog-bear digging hard in the moist, warm earth, and snuffing as it digged. Then the branches closed over his head again, and Kala Nag began to go down into the valley — not quietly this time, but as a runaway gun goes down a steep bank — in one rush. The huge limbs moved as steadily as pistons, eight feet to each stride, and the wrinkled skin of the elbow-points rustled. The undergrowth on either side of him ripped with a noise like torn canvas, and the saplings that he heaved away right and left with his shoulders sprang back again, and banged him on the flank, and great trails of creepers, all matted together, hung from his tusks as he threw his head from side to side and ploughed out his pathway.

Then Little Toomai laid himself down close to the great neck, lest a swinging bough should sweep him to the ground, and he wished that he were back in the lines again. The grass began to get squashy, and Kala Nag's feet sucked and squelched as he put them down, and the night mist at the bottom of the valley chilled Little Toomai.

There was a splash and a trample, and the rush of running water, and Kala Nag strode through the bed of a river, feeling his way at each step. Above the noise of the water, as it swirled round the elephant's legs, Little Toomai could hear more splashing and some trumpeting both upstream and down — great grunts and angry snortings, and all the mist about him seemed to be full of rolling, wavy shadows.

"*Ai!*" he said, half aloud, his teeth chattering. "The elephant-folk are out to-night. It *is* the dance, then."

Kala Nag swashed out of the water, blew his trunk clear, and began another climb; but this time he was not alone, and he had not to make his path. That was made already, six feet wide, in front of him, where the bent jungle-grass was trying to recover itself and stand up. Many elephants must have gone that way only a few minutes before. Little Toomai looked back, and behind him a great wild tusker, with his little pig's eyes glowing like hot coals, was just lifting himself out of the misty river. Then the trees closed up again, and they went on and up, with trumpetings and crashings, and the sound of breaking branches on every side of them.

At last Kala Nag stood still between two tree-trunks at the very top of the hill. They were part of a circle of trees that grew round an irregular space of some three or four acres, and in all that space, as Little Toomai could see, the ground had been trampled down as hard as a brick floor. Some trees grew in the centre of the clearing, but their bark was rubbed away, and the white wood beneath showed all shiny and polished in the patches of moonlight. There were creepers hanging from the upper branches, and the bells of the flowers of the creepers, great waxy white things like convolvuluses, hung down fast asleep; but within the limits of the clearing there was not a single blade of green — nothing but the trampled earth. The moonlight showed it all iron-gray, except where some elephants stood upon it, and their shadows were inky black.

Little Toomai looked, holding his breath, with his eyes starting out of his head, and as he looked, more and more and more elephants swung out into the open from between the tree-trunks. Little Toomai could only count up to ten, and he counted again and again on his fingers till he lost count of the tens, and his head began to swim. Outside the clearing he could hear them crashing in the undergrowth as they worked their way up the hillside; but as soon as they were within the circle of the tree-trunks they moved like ghosts.

There were white-tusked wild males, with fallen leaves and nuts and twigs lying in the wrinkles of their necks and the folds of their ears; fat, slow-footed she-elephants, with restless little pinky-black calves only three or four feet high running under their stomachs; young elephants with their tusks just beginning to show, and very

155

proud of them; lanky, scraggy old-maid elephants, with their hollow, anxious faces, and trunks like rough bark; savage old bull-elephants, scarred from shoulder to flank with great weals and cuts of bygone fights, and the caked dirt of their solitary mud-baths dropping from their shoulders; and there was one with a broken tusk and the marks of the full-stroke, the terrible drawing scrape, of a tiger's claws on his side. They were standing head to head, or walking to and fro across the ground in couples, or rocking and swaying all by themselves — scores and scores of elephants. Toomai knew that so long as he lay still on Kala Nag's neck nothing would happen to him; for even in the rush and scramble of a Keddah-drive a wild elephant does not reach up with his trunk and drag a man off the neck of a tame elephant; and these elephants were not thinking of men that night.

Once they started and put their ears forward when they heard the chinking of a leg-iron in the forest, but it was Pudmini, Petersen Sahib's pet elephant, her chain snapped short off, grunting, snuffling up the hillside. She must have broken her pickets, and come straight from Petersen Sahib's camp; and Little Toomai saw another elephant, one that he did not know, with deep rope-galls on his back and breast. He, too, must have run away from some camp in the hills about.

At last there was no sound of any more elephants moving in the forest, and Kala Nag rolled out from his station between the trees and went into the middle of the crowd, clucking and gurgling, and all the elephants began to talk in their own tongue, and to move about. Still lying down, Little Toomai looked down upon scores and scores of broad backs, and wagging ears, and tossing trunks, and little rolling eyes. He heard the click of tusks as they crossed other tusks by accident, and the dry rustle of trunks twined together, and the chafing of enormous sides and shoulders in the crowd, and the incessant flick and *hissh* of the great tails. Then a cloud came over the moon, and he sat in black darkness; but the quiet, steady hustling and pushing and gurgling went on just the same. He knew that there were elephants all round Kala Nag, and that there was no chance of backing him out of the assembly; so he set his teeth and shivered. In a Keddah at least there was torch-light and shouting, but here he was all alone in the dark, and once a trunk came up and touched him on the knee. Then an elephant trumpeted, and they all took it up for five or ten terrible seconds.

The dew from the trees above spattered down like rain on the unseen backs, and a dull booming noise began, not very loud at first, and Little Toomai could not tell what it was; but it grew and grew, and Kala Nag lifted up one fore foot and then the other, and brought them down on the ground — one-two, one-two, as steadily as trip-hammers. The elephants were stamping all together now, and it sounded like a war-drum beaten at the mouth of a cave.

The dew fell from the trees till there was no more left to fall, and the booming went on, and the ground rocked and shivered, and Little Toomai put his hands up to his ears to shut out the sound. But it was all one gigantic jar that ran through him — this stamp of hundreds of heavy feet on the raw earth. Once or twice he could

feel Kala Nag and all the others surge forward a few strides, and the thumping would change to the crushing sound of juicy green things being bruised, but in a minute or two the boom of feet on hard earth began again. A tree was creaking and groaning somewhere near him. He put out his arm, and felt the bark, but Kala Nag moved forward, still tramping, and he could not tell where he was in the clearing. There was no sound from the elephants, except once, when two or three little calves squeaked together. Then he heard a thump and a shuffle, and the booming went on. It must have lasted fully two hours, and Little Toomai ached in every nerve; but he knew by the smell of the night air that the dawn was coming.

The morning broke in one sheet of pale yellow behind the green hills, and the booming stopped with the first ray, as though the light had been an order. Before Little Toomai had got the ringing out of his head, before even he had shifted his position, there was not an elephant in sight except Kala Nag, Pudmini, and the elephant with the rope-galls, and there was neither sign nor rustle nor whisper down the hillsides to show where the others had gone. Little Toomai stared again and again. The clearing, as he remembered it, had grown in the night. More trees stood in the middle of it, but the undergrowth and the jungle-grass at the sides had been rolled back. Little Toomai stared once more. Now he understood the trampling. The elephants had stamped out more room — had stamped the thick grass and juicy cane to trash, the trash into slivers, the slivers into tiny fibres, and the fibres into hard earth.

"Wah!" said Little Toomai, and his eyes were very heavy. "Kala Nag, my lord, let us keep by Pudmini and go to Petersen Sahib's camp, or I shall drop from thy neck."

The third elephant watched the two go away, snorted, wheeled round, and took his own path. He may have belonged to some little native king's establishment, fifty or sixty or a hundred miles away.

Two hours later, as Petersen Sahib was eating early breakfast, the elephants, who had been double-chained that night, began to trumpet, and Pudmini, mired to the shoulders, with Kala Nag, very foot-sore, shambled into the camp. Little Toomai's face was gray and pinched, and his hair was full of leaves and drenched with dew; but he tried to salute Petersen Sahib, and cried faintly: "The dance — the elephant-dance! I have seen it, and — I die!" As Kala Nag sat down, he slid off his neck in a dead faint.

161

THE LION

by Jim Kjelgaard

When Jim Kjelgaard's father moved the young Kjelgaard family from New York City to a Pennsylvania farm, Jim and his two brothers (one of whom became a forester) were as happy as Br'er Rabbit tossed into the briar patch. "Between intervals of attending school," says the author, "we ran trap lines, shot deer, and fished for trout." When they were older, they had a rough hunting-lodge of their own, and from it went out shooting grouse and squirrels.

Jim Kjelgaard, in a variety of jobs — farm hand, factory worker, surveyor's assistant, teamster, plumber's helper, — learnt a great deal about his country and served a useful apprenticeship for his ultimate profession of writing. Since his first book in 1941, *Forest Patrol*, he has published a long roster of stories about dogs and horses, wild and tame; about stags, coyotes, cougars, seals, and even a polar bear. He lives now in Arizona, the setting for *Lion Hound*, from which this story comes.

Anyone who, touring in certain parts of the United States, has been puzzled and outraged at the mentality of service station owners who could use a captive cougar (which is the proper name of this "lion") to draw custom, will take satisfaction in the conclusion of this story.

The lion's mind was filled with memories and his heart with hate.

He was full-grown now, a supple, sinewy creature at the very height of his powers and in the fullness of his life. He weighed well over two hundred pounds. Only in early Indian days, when game was everywhere in profusion, had bigger mountain lions roamed the rimrock. They had grown larger then because there had been an abundance of food and because hound packs, unknown until the white men brought them, had not hunted lions over the colored bluffs and rises.

This lion had also had all the food he could eat, but much of it was not food that he had hunted. Nor had his life pattern been that of any other lion on the rim.

He had been the first cub of a sleek young lioness who had prowled far and wide to find a safe den high on the side of a towering mountain. There he had been born, a squirming little spotted cub that might have nestled with room to spare in a man's cupped hands. But every day, and almost every hour, he grew bigger. Having only one cub, and finding good hunting, his mother had given him all the milk he could use.

Gradually he became more independent. It had become his consuming ambition to catch a deer, as he had seen his mother do, and he was forever stalking them. But his hunting technique was far short of perfection. He was too eager, and he either betrayed himself by some ill-timed move or started his rush too soon. Though he did catch a couple of rabbits, and numberless grasshoppers, it was early autumn before he pulled down his first live deer and that was accidental.

163

The lioness had gone on her stalk, which was familiar routine now. The cub heard the startled deer in wild flight when she rushed them. Then a fawn, fleeing without looking where it was going, almost overran the cub. He had only to meet it head-on and bear it down while the fawn rolled helplessly on its side.

It was a lucky encounter for the cub. A full-grown deer might have killed him, but the fawn was as inexperienced as its attacker. The cub imbedded all four taloned feet firmly in the little deer and his strong jaws sought the backbone. He bit as hard as he could, and when his teeth met through the spinal column the fawn lay still.

When the lioness, who had missed her strike, came back to the cub, he was crouched over his kill, growling at her. Angered, she took all the fight out of him with one swipe of her paw and the cub and mother fed side by side. But he had learned.

Snow fell, and the pair remained together as they prowled the wilderness. Sometimes they ate well and sometimes they went hungry, for the deer upon which they depended for the bulk of their food were neither as plentiful nor as incautious as they had been during the summer. With the approach of winter, many of the deer had gone into the lowlands and the lioness was reluctant to follow them there.

Hunger finally drove her to it, but she changed her hunting methods radically and the cub could not at first understand this. While living in the heights, they had gone where they pleased when they pleased. Here the lioness would hunt only at night. She was careful to avoid the ranches and the scattered homes, and kept strictly to the thickets where deer herds would winter through. But there were many more deer here and the lions' bellies were usually filled.

One day, after they had fed and were resting in a thicket, the lioness raised her sleek head. Because he was accustomed to doing exactly as she did, the cub looked where she was looking. The thicket was on a canyon's rim, and on the other side of the canyon walked a creature such as the cub had never seen before. It seemed a slow and plodding thing, with no harm in it, or even much of interest. The cub had seen his first man.

When it came, disaster was sudden.

The lioness had killed a deer during the night, and she and the cub had fed well. With daylight they entered a thicket about a half mile from the kill and curled up to rest. All morning they were undisturbed, but when the sun slanted past high noon the cub heard a sound which he had never heard before.

It was a mournful, rolling noise, and somehow terrifying; for the cub felt the hairs on his neck prickle. He did not know that he was hearing the bay of a hound on cold scent, but he did know that the sound originated very near the kill his mother had made last night.

Without hesitation the lioness slipped out the opposite side of the thicket, and began to run, the cub following. They did not run fast because, though lions are capable of amazing speed for a distance of a few yards, they cannot run very fast for very long. They loped along as best as they could, while behind them the uncertain baying of the hound sent echoes back from distant heights.

Suddenly the hound's baying was no longer sporadic, but sharp,

eager, steady. He had found the thicket where the lioness and her cub had rested, and had hot scent now. The tonguing of a second dog mingled with that of the first.

The lioness ran faster, and there was an air of desperate fear about her now that communicated itself to the cub. Never before had he known his mother to be afraid of anything, and the certain fear that he could now sense gave added speed to his own feet.

The tonguing hounds sounded nearer and nearer, but when his mother whipped around with her back to a big tree, the cub ran blindly on. He did not know where he was going, but only that he must go. There was nothing that could have made him stop.

He heard the running hounds halt, their steady tonguing coming only from the place where his mother had stopped. One of the hounds voiced a high-pitched shriek of agony, then only one continued to tongue. After a few moments that one screamed, too.

The cub heard the blast of a rifle and then all was silence.

He did not stop because he was too terrified, and that was his salvation. Both dogs were dead, disemboweled by the lioness, and the man who shot her could not overtake the laboring cub alone.

When the cub finally did stop, too winded to run another step, he was miles from the place where his mother had made her stand against the dogs. He was still frightened and very worried, for

167

never before had he been alone. But not for any reason would he go back. His mother, he thought, would join him here.

The cub whimpered lonesomely to himself, as he sought the shelter of an evergreen thicket. The long run had exhausted him completely, and though he was hungry, he was too tired to look for any food. He lay down beneath the evergreens and slept.

When he awakened he was still bewildered and worried because his mother was not with him, but returning to look for her was too terrifying a prospect. The dogs might be there. Starting out to hunt, the cub found and made a clumsy rush at a herd of deer. They avoided him easily, as did all the others he stalked that day and night. Three days passed before the cub fed, and then luck directed him once more.

During the hunting season, an unskilled hunter had shot at a handsome buck, but only wounded it. The buck ran a long way before its strength began to fail. Then it weakened fast, and almost anything could have pulled it down when the cub stumbled across it. The cub stayed near his kill until it was all eaten, then started out again.

At first his luck was bad and he knew more hunger. Then he found the kill of another lion, fed at it, and hastily ran away, sensing that he was trespassing and would be punished if caught.

The cub had more luck in an area where hunters had killed several deer and left their offal in the snow. It was cold and frozen, and not at all what he liked, but it sustained life. Then, little by little, forced by necessity, his hunting skill improved. Though he still missed a good many strikes at deer, he made enough kills so that he did not grow thin or too weak to fight the bitter weather. By mid-winter he was a fairly skilled hunter.

Then the hounds came again.

The cub was lying up on a rocky ledge, trying to absorb such warmth as could be found in the winter sun, when he heard them begin to tongue near a kill he had left the previous night. Immediately he knew panic. This was the second time he had heard hounds, and as far as he knew there was no greater danger. In long, springing leaps he sped away over the snow, and as before he paid little attention to where he was going. His sole idea was to put distance between the hounds and himself.

He heard their desultory cold trail barks change to eager yelling as they came to the ledge where he had lain up. Desperately he tried to increase his pace and succeeded only in running himself

nearly breathless. The cub leaped at the trunk of a pine, drew himself up, climbed halfway to the top, and tried to flatten himself against the tree.

He heard the hounds come, and because he was born curious he could not resist peeking around the tree trunk at them. Four black and tan brutes, they gathered beneath the tree and made the air hideous with their yelling while they leaped upward and fell back. The cub breathed a little easier. He hadn't been sure he'd be safe even in a tree, but obviously the hounds couldn't climb trees.

Twenty minutes later three men arrived and the cub peered wonderingly at them. He'd had almost nothing to do with men aside from having seen one across a canyon and running across their tracks now and again. But there had been nothing in his experience to prove that men were dangerous; the dogs seemed far more to be feared.

"It's just a cub!" one of the men yelled. "Tie up the dogs and we'll take him alive!"

Amazed, the cub watched two of the men catch the dogs and tie them to trees. He scanned the men carefully, and had a first uneasy premonition that he had underestimated them. But even though he was frightened he was still curious enough to want to see for himself what was going on.

A coil of rope around his shoulder, one of the men began climbing the tree. The cub started up the trunk, then changed his mind and crawled out on a branch. But when the branch swayed and bent beneath his weight, he became afraid he would fall and stopped to hold on with all four paws. Instinctively he parted his jaws in a snarl. To his great relief the climbing man did not come out on the branch at all, but continued up the trunk. The cub shifted nervous eyes from the chained dogs to the men on the ground, and back to the man in the tree.

The climbing man was above him now, bracing his feet against a branch and resting his back on the trunk. The coil of rope was in his hands, and he swung a loop. The cub saw it coming. He spat and tried to lash at it with a front paw, but, when he did, the branch on which he crouched swayed alarmingly and he had to give all his attention just to holding on. The loop settled over his head and tightened about his neck. The cub was jerked from his perch.

He wriggled his body, waved his paws, and above all tried to draw breath. But though he could wriggle, his whole weight hung on the rope around his neck, choking him. His tongue dangled out and his head pounded. For a moment or two he was unconscious.

Then, finally, he was stretched on the snow with his paws tied together and a stick clamped between his jaws. Helpless, he could do little except roll his eyes. He looked in turn at each of the three men, and at the hounds. His bound paws were tied to a long green pole and the cub was suspended, head downward, while two of the men supported the pole on their shoulders. The third led the leashed dogs.

The cub's only conscious emotion was overwhelming fear, but beneath the fear was hate. His paws were bound so tightly that they hurt him, and the stick in his jaws squeezed a part of his tongue against a sharp tooth. The hatred he was to feel toward all men was born in that moment.

For an hour and a half the men carrying him plodded through the snow, stopping occasionally to put their burden down and rest. They reached a highway, and the cub was unceremoniously dumped into the back of a pickup truck. The truck was run into a unheated garage, and the cub left there all night long.

Early the next morning his journey was resumed. Far down the highway he was taken, out of the wilderness where he had been born and into settled country. At first the cub shivered every time they passed another car; then he became used to them and did not flinch any more. Even the rumble of heavy trucks did not disturb him unduly. Finally the truck stopped, and the driver got out.

"I've got a lion for you, Tom," he said.

"Good," a strange voice answered. "Let's see him."

The cub was lifted out of the truck and could look about him. There was a building nearby such as he had never seen before, and a couple of automobiles parked in front of it. A ring of curious people gathered. The cub could not know that he had been brought to a filling station, nor read the sign which explained why he had been brought here: STOP! LOOK AT THE LIVE MOUNTAIN LION!

The cub knew only that there were smells here which he did not like because they hurt his nostrils, and too many of the man-creatures which he hated. He was carried to a kennel, where a strong leather collar attached to a chain was strapped about his neck. Then the man who had brought him here cut the ropes that bound his paws and held the stick in his jaws. The man leaped clear.

He was in no danger. The cub wanted only to get out of sight and leaped at once into the kennel, the only hiding place he could see. For the first time since his capture he knew some measure of comfort. There had been another lion here before him, and judging by the scent, it had been a very old beast. The cub could not know that it had died, or that he was taking its place as an attraction for the filling station.

Not until night, when everything was quiet, did he venture out of the kennel. He sniffed suspiciously at a bowl of horse meat that had been placed within his reach, and licked at it. But he was still too nervous and excited to be hungry. He padded as far as the chain would let him go and looked longingly at a cluster of pines across the road. He could smell them too, the only link with the wilderness home he loved so well.

The next morning he was in the kennel when he heard a car stop and the voices of people. He saw them bending and peering in the door, and he cowered in the farthest corner. Then the filling station owner brought a long pole with a hook on the end. He hooked a link of the chain and dragged the cub out into the open, bruising the lion's side against the kennel door. While the man held him, another man slid a board over the kennel door so the cub could not get back in.

The people backed away. The cub slunk around the corner of his kennel and lay uneasily while his side throbbed and hurt him. Fear still ruled him, but mingled with it was a rising resentment. Even while he wished there was some place he might hide, the end of the cub's tail twitched menacingly.

It took him a month to become adjusted, so that he would eat every night and of his own accord venture out of the kennel by day. He had already discovered, after several desperate attempts while the friendly night shielded him, that the chain and collar could not be broken, so he had stopped trying. He had also found that, though he detested everything about the place, apparently he was meant to come to no harm here.

The cub lay in front or on top of the kennel and blinked what appeared to be sleepy eyes at the many people who came to stare at him. The people could not have been more mistaken. While they looked at him, the cub studied them. He knew they were dangerous because people had made him a captive, but they had their weak points, too.

Spring came and summer followed and winter came again, and still the cub lay near the kennel watching people, and studying their habits. Because he always had plenty to eat, the cub grew as no wild lion can hope to grow.

Every night, after the filling station was closed and there were few cars on the highway, the lion stood before his kennel and stared at the pines across the road. When he did he became tense and alive, and his eyes were anything but sleepy. He never lost the fierce desire to be free of his chain and back in the wilderness, but not until he had been a captive for three years did his chance come.

The summer sun was hot in the sky one day and the lion was dozing in front of the kennel when a big blue car stopped at the filling station. There were a man and woman in the front seat, and a big black and tan dog in the back. Almost before the car stopped, the dog had leaped through a window and was rushing at the lion.

No longer a fearful cub, but fully grown, the big lion waited, crouched and snarling. The dog leaped toward him, and the lion waited, until it was impossible for the dog to get back to safety. Then he slapped a front paw to either side of the dog's head, bit through its brain, and the fight was over almost before it started.

The lion drew back to get more slack in his chain for, brandishing a thermos bottle, the man was shrieking and rushing at him now. There was a shouted warning from the filling station's owner, and the hysterical tourist stopped just short of any place the chained lion could reach.

Angered, the animal leaped anyhow. He went up and out, feeling the chain tighten behind him as he sprang. The chain held, but the leather collar was now old and worn. The collar snapped, and the lion bore the white-faced tourist down. He would have killed him there had he not instantly realized that the freedom he longed for was now his. The lion sprang across the highway into the pines.

When he came to the end of the pines, he crossed a field and found himself in a forest of hardwoods. At the far side of the forest he slowed to a walk, and that night he feasted on a sheep which he took easily from a bleating flock. Fortunately for him, neither the farmer nor the filling station owner thought of putting an experienced lion hunter with trained hounds on his trail, and the volunteer hunters were soon left far behind.

The lion traveled on, but after the first day he moved only at night and lay up when the sun shone. His captivity had taught

173

him much, and among the things he had learned was the fact that humans can see or sense little in the dark. At night he felt perfectly safe, and often walked within feet of houses in his path. Once, after midnight, he padded right through a village.

Twice on his long journey he was attacked by farm dogs that snarled out at him. They were mere annoyances. Though the lion had learned by experience that he must never again run up a tree when dogs were on his trail, he was not afraid of any one dog. Leaving the dogs where he killed them, the lion continued his journey. He did not like this country and would not stay in it.

He took his food where he found it: sheep, calves, and once a horse. By this time he was far enough from the filling station so that news of his escape had not preceded him, and the killings were ascribed to packs of wild dogs which infested the country.

Two weeks after his escape, the lion stalked and killed his first deer. He made no mistakes in the stalk and he did not miss the final strike. His early hunting training had come back to him, the journey had toughened him, and he was no cub now, but a fully mature mountain lion. But, even though there were deer in it, this country was still too settled for his taste. He went on until he reached the rimrock, and there he was content to stay.

He had learned a great deal about men and their ways, and he understood how to use that knowledge. A sullen, dangerous beast, he was prepared to make the rimrock his kingdom, to hold it against all challengers, and to raid wherever he wished.

SHILLINGS FROM THE FON

by Gerald Durrell

The Fon is the king of Bafut, a part of the Cameroons to which Gerald Durrell has been on several very successful animal collecting expeditions. On this occasion described in *The Bafut Beagles* the Fon, who normally wears elaborate robes and is surrounded by his court with all the ritual of his position, arrives dressed as a hunter, bare but for a white loincloth, to enjoy a day "off duty" with his English friend. The galagos may be better known to readers as bush babies; The "beef" to which they refer, in the pidgin English which is their common language, means wild animals!

He led me out of the environs of his compound, along the road for perhaps half a mile, and then branched off through some maize-fields. He walked at a great pace, twirling his spear and humming to himself, occasionally turning to grin at me with a mischievous delight illuminating his features. Presently we left the fields, passed through a small thicket of mimbo palms, dark and mysterious and full of the rustling of the fronds, and then started to climb up the golden hillside. When we reached the top, the Fon paused, stuck his spear into the ground, folded his arms and surveyed the view. I had stopped a little way down the hillside to collect some delicately coloured snails; when I had arrived at the top, the Fon appeared to have gone into a trance. Presently he sighed deeply, and, turning towards me, smiled and swept his arms wide.

"Na my country dis," he said, "na foine, dis country."

I nodded in agreement, and we stood there in silence for a few minutes and looked at the view. Below us lay a mosaic of small fields, green and silver and fawn, broken up by mimbo palm thickets and an occasional patch of rust red where the earth of a field had been newly hoed. This small area of cultivation was like a coloured handkerchief laid on the earth and forgotten, surrounded on all sides by the great ocean of mountains, their crests gilded and their valleys smudged with shadow by the falling sun. The Fon gazed slowly round, an expression on his face that was a mixture of affection and child-like pleasure. He sighed again, a sigh of satisfaction.

"Foine!" he murmured. Then he plucked his spear from the earth and led the way down into the next valley, humming tunefully to himself.

The valley was shallow and flat, thickly overgrown with a wood

175

of small stunted trees, some only about ten feet high. Many of them were completely invisible under immense cloaks of convolvulus, squat towers of trembling leaves and ivory-coloured flowers. The valley had captured the sunshine of the day, and the warm air was heavy and sweet with the scent of flowers and leaves. A sleepy throbbing drone came from a thousand bees that hovered round the flowers; a tiny anonymous bird let a melodious trickle of song fill the valley, and then stopped suddenly, so that the only sound was the blurred singing of the bees again, as they hovered round the trees or waddled up the smooth tunnel of the convolvulus flowers. The Fon surveyed the trees for a moment, and then moved quietly through the grass to a better vantage point, where our view into the wood was not so clogged with convolvulus.

"Na for here we go see beef," he whispered, pointing at the trees; "we sit down an' wait small time."

He squatted down on his haunches and waited in relaxed immobility; I squatted down beside him and found my attention equally divided between watching him and watching the trees. As the trees remained devoid of life, I concentrated on my companion. He sat there, clutching his spear upright in his large hands, and on his face was a look of eager expectancy, like that of a child at a pantomime before the curtain goes up. When he had appeared out of that dark little hut in Bafut, it seemed as though he had not only left behind his robes and trappings of state, but that he had also shed that regal air which had seemed so much part of his character. Here, crouching in this quiet, warm valley with his spear, he appeared to be just another hunter, his bright dark eyes fixed on the trees, waiting for the quarry he knew would come. But, as I looked at him, I realised that he was not just another hunter; there was something different about him which I could not place. It came to me what it was: any ordinary hunter would have crouched there, patient, a trifle bored, for he would have done the same thing so many times before. But the Fon waited, his eyes gleaming, a half-smile on his wide mouth, and I realised that he was thoroughly enjoying himself. I wondered how many times in the past he had become tired of his deferential councillors and his worshipping subjects, and felt his magnificent robes to be hot and cumbersome and his pointed shoes cramping and hard. Then perhaps the urge had come to him to feel the soft red earth under his bare feet and the wind on his naked body, so that he would steal off to his hut,

176

put on the clothes of a hunter and stride away over the hills, twirling his spear and humming, pausing on the hilltops to admire the beautiful country over which he ruled. I remembered the words he had spoken to me only a short time before, "If a man has hunting for his eyes, his nose and his blood, he never gets too old to go to bush." The Fon, I decided, was definitely one of that sort of men. My meditations on the Fon's character were interrupted: he leant forward and gripped my arm, pointing a long finger at the trees.

"Dey done come," he whispered, his face wreathed in smiles.

I followed the pointing of his finger, and for a moment I could see nothing but a confused net of branches. Then something moved, and I saw the animal that we had been awaiting.

It came drifting through the tangled branches with all the gentle, airy grace of a piece of thistledown. When it got nearer, I discovered that it looked exactly like my idea of a leprechaun: it was clad in a little fur coat of greenish-grey, and it had a long, slender, furry tail. Its hands, which were pink, were large for its size, and its fingers tremendously long and attenuated. Its ears were large and the skin so fine that it was semi-transparent; these ears seemed to have a life of their own, for they twisted and turned independently, sometimes crumpling and folding flat to the head as if they were a fan, at others standing up pricked and straight like anaemic arum lilies. The face of the little creature was dominated by a pair of tremendous dark eyes, eyes that would have put any self-respecting owl to shame. Moreover, the creature could twist its head round and look

over its back in much the same way that an owl does. It ran to the tip of a slender branch that scarcely dipped beneath its weight, and there it sat, clutching the bark with its long, slender fingers, peering about with its great eyes and chirruping dimly to itself. It was, I knew, a galago, but it looked much more like something out of a fairy tale.

It sat on the branch, twittering vaguely to itself, for about a minute; then an astonishing thing happened. Quite suddenly the trees were full of galagos, galagos of every age and size, ranging from those little bigger than a walnut to adults that could have fitted themselves

quite comfortably into an ordinary drinking-glass. They jumped
from branch to branch, grasping the leaves and twigs with their
large, thin hands, twittering softly to each other and gazing round
them with the wide-eyed innocence of a troupe of cherubim. The
baby ones, who seemed to be composed almost entirely of eyes,
kept fairly close to their parents; occasionally they would sit up
on their hind legs and hold up their tiny pink hands, fingers spread
wide, as though in horror at the depravity they were seeing in the
world of leaves around them.

179

One of these babies discovered, while I watched, that he was sitting on the same branch as a large and succulent locust. It was evening time, and the insect was drowsy and slow to realise its danger. Before it could do anything, the baby galago had flitted down the branch and grabbed it firmly round the middle. The locust

woke up abruptly and decided that something must be done. It was a large insect, and was, in fact, almost as big as the baby galago; also it possessed a pair of long and muscular hind legs, and it started to kick out vigorously with them. It was a fascinating fight to watch: the galago clasped the locust desperately in his long fingers, and tried to bite it. Each time he tried to bite, the locust would give a terrific kick with its hind legs and knock its adversary off balance, so he would fall off the branch and hang beneath, suspended by his feet. When this had happened several times, I decided that the galago must have adhesive soles. And even when hanging upside down and being kicked in the stomach by a large locust, he maintained his expression of wide-eyed innocence.

The end of the fight was unexpected: when they were hanging upside down, the locust gave an extra hefty kick, and the galago's feet lost their grip, so that they fell through the leaves clasped together. As they tumbled earthwards, the galago loosened one hand from his grip round the locust's waist and grabbed a passing branch with the effortless ease of a trained acrobat. He hauled himself on to the branch and bit the locust's head off before the insect could recover sufficiently to continue the fight. Holding the decapitated but still kicking body in one hand, the galago stuffed the insect's head into his mouth and chewed it with evident enjoyment. Then he sat, clasping the twitching body in one hand, and contemplated it with his head on one side, giving vent to shrill and excited screams of delight. When the corpse had ceased to move and the big hind legs had stiffened in death, the galago tore them off, one by one, and ate them. He looked ridiculously like a diminutive elderly gourmet, clasping in one hand the drumstick of some gigantic chicken.

Soon the valley was filled with shadow and it became difficult to see the galagos among the leaves, though we could hear their soft chittering. We rose from our cramped positions and made our way back up the hillside. At the top the Fon paused and gazed down at the woods below, smiling delightedly.

"Dat beef!" he chuckled, "I like um too much. All time 'e make funny for me, an' I go laugh."

"Na fine beef," I said. "How you call um?"

"For Bafut," said the Fon, "we call um Shilling."

"You think sometimes my hunter men fit catch some?"

"Tomorrow you go have some," promised the Fon, but he would

not tell me how they were to be captured, nor who was to do the capturing. We reached Bafut in the dusk, and when the Fon was respectably clothed once more he came and had a drink. As I said good night to him, I reminded him of his promise to get me some of the galagos.

"Yes, my friend, I no go forget," he said. "I go get you some Shilling."

Four days passed, and I began to think that either the Fon had forgotten, or else the creatures were proving more difficult to capture than he had imagined. Then, on the fifth morning, my tea was brought in, and reposing on the tray was a small, highly-coloured raffia basket. I pulled off the lid and looked sleepily inside, and four pairs of enormous, liquid, innocent eyes peered up at me with expressions of gentle inquiry.

It was a basketful of Shillings from the Fon.

TOM, THE GRIZZLY

by Olai Aslagsson

As a boy Olai Aslagsson was filled with an overwhelming urge for adventure which took him to sea and so to America where, after years of restless wandering, he at last found himself at peace in the prairies and mountains of Montana and Wyoming. Here, as a trapper and shepherd, he learnt to know and appreciate the wild animals. Here, too, in primitive surroundings and far from human company, he started to write his first stories. Now he is living once more in his native Norway but he still returns to his prairie friends and experiences in his writing as for the setting of his book *Tom, the Grizzly* from which this extract is taken.

After Bimbo's death the Englishman no longer wanted to catch the grizzly alive. He was determined to kill the beast, so determined that he suggested a hunt, for the very next day. The others tried to dissuade him. They said that on foot they would merely make the bear even more cautious and perhaps chase him away altogether. They argued that since it had proved impossible to hunt him down on horseback in open country, a new approach would have to be found. They pointed out that spring guns and poison had not yet been tried. And they stressed the importance of the bear returning to the ranch.

The winter grew harder, storms succeeded each other and the snow kept mounting. Tom had not many choices left. As there was hardly any food in the wilderness, he could not avoid coming close to the ranch. However, the bad weather helped him in one respect. As long as it was not too cold and the snow level was still moderate, the herds of cattle were left to fend for themselves. Otherwise, they had to be fed hay and therefore could not be pastured far away from the ranch. No food on earth would bring the bear willingly out of the forest on sunny days. Thus the bad weather made things somewhat easier for him. Life was again worth living.

In the whole area Tom was the only bear not to have crawled into his den to hibernate. On his nightly raids he was often accompanied by starved coyotes which, unable to kill cattle themselves, kept close to him in the hope that his leftovers would provide them with food.

Tom hated company and shunned it whenever he could. He wanted to be alone. The coyotes never held their tongues. He abhorred them heartily, but he was helpless, and yet it was the greed of these animals which one night saved his life and taught him to beware of things of which he had no experience. It was a starlit, bitterly cold night. There was a faint shimmer on the snow. With two famished coyotes as onlookers, the bear stole among the cows and killed a calf. However, he found himself in trouble. The animals

were restless and made a dreadful noise. Before Tom had managed to carry off his prey, two horsemen appeared and the bear had to run and hide in the dry bed of a creek.

But he was furious and hungry and went no farther than he thought was strictly necessary. When he found he was not being tracked, he sneaked back and came so close that he could see the calf he had killed. Though there was little light there was enough for his sharp eyes. He clearly saw the riders approaching the calf on their ponies. He was angrily afraid that the men would outwit him and rob him of his prey. They left the calf where it was when at last they rode away. Still, Tom was mistrustful. He took his time. He knew he would have to look for traps before he could appease his appetite.

The coyotes, however, could not afford to take their time. Having to be on their guard against both the bear and the men, they apparently assumed that the bear was their most dangerous adversary at the moment because he might deprive them of a meal unless they acted first. Their hunger made them foolhardy and, as soon as the riders were out of sight, they fell upon the calf.

Exasperated at the two coyotes stealing his legitimate property, Tom would, in normal circumstances, have attacked both. That is what he actually wanted to do now. But he considered the presence of men and their limitless ingenuity. His wrath subsided and he was filled with ugly curiosity. He could save himself the trouble of looking for traps. The coyotes would do the job for him. All that he himself had to do was to watch them closely. He would get the calf once he had convinced himself that the men had not devised any new traps. Keeping cool and calm as usual, he bided his time. The calf was big enough for three meals and giving up a few morsels was better than taking a chance.

In the darkness, the coyotes, being smaller than the bear, had less to fear from a rifle. They tried hard to devour as much as possible before they had to leave. Time was precious. Anticipating the bear's return, they were not as cautious as usual. Since they did not know in what condition the bear had left his prey, their suspicion was not aroused when they found the carcass with its belly open. Gluttonous, they did not scent steel. They only smelled blood. They tore at the vitals of the dead animal without worrying about anything but the bear's return.

When Tom was at last satisfied there was no danger, he sneaked nearer. He was in no hurry. He stopped and inhaled the cold air.

He remained motionless for quite some time, listening for noises that might be man's footsteps on frozen snow. But everything was quiet and the snow merely creaked under his own paws. Now and then a starved coyote howled.

Moving along the bottom of the dry creek, he hid so well that even the coyotes would not have seen him had they taken time off to check where he was. He had come so close that he was able to discern in detail what was going on. The coyotes were gorging without looking and Tom was so furious that he was about to leave the creek to join the plunderers when something startled him.

Squealing, one of the two coyotes suddenly withdrew his head from the carcass and collapsed, groaning with pain. The pain at once became so violent that he could not lie still, but began to thrash about like an eel. At times he howled frightfully and then, raving, he drove his fangs into his own belly. When the pains had reached their climax, the coyote uttered no sound but made very

odd leaps. Then he fell to the ground with foam at his muzzle, the other coyote staring at him without understanding.

Tom, too, did not understand what was going on. He watched apprehensively. His amazement changed into horror when the other coyote, which had not moved so far, began to behave like his companion. The bear, though uneasy, at the same time felt curious. Of course, he had seen death before, but he had never witnessed a struggle of this kind. He approached the animals with fear and expectation.

The coyote which had been stricken first died with a groan, while the other performed a strangely jerky dance. The bear was fascinated. A short while ago he had detested the two coyotes because he could not get rid of them. He would have liked to knock out their brains. But now he felt neither hatred nor a desire for vengeance, nor compassion. He was merely surprised and inquisitive. He remembered his original intention only when both coyotes sprawled dead in the snow.

The tragedy of the winter night had had no effect on his appetite. However, his instinct for examining everything and his deep rooted mistrust prevented him from feeding on the carcass right away. Noticing traces of men, he was even warier than usual and discovered a faint unfamiliar smell when he put his muzzle where the coyotes had been eating. This scent had nothing in common with coyotes or men and it was so faint that he would not have been aware of it under ordinary circumstances. As the situation was, however, he caught it strongly.

Tom withdrew his head growling. He was alarmed and suspicious. Instinctively he felt that this disturbing smell had something to do with the death of the coyotes. With these misgivings, proof was only a short way off. His brain worked purposefully. With resolute steps he went to the coyotes, sniffed at their muzzles, and found what he had been looking for. He growled deeply and returned to the carcass to check once more. The result of his investigations must have been satisfactory because after a few moments he suddenly turned his back on the poisoned carcass and started heaping snow on to it.

What the tomb of the unfortunate calf lacked in depth was made up in height and width. Having finished his work, the bear growled approvingly. The peace of death reigned in the countryside, but later in the same night other coyotes would come, attracted by the frozen bodies of their hapless mates. They would see the mound of snow and no doubt examine it. Perhaps they would feed on the carcass and follow their brethren to the happy hunting grounds where there is no cold or hunger. Perhaps, however, they would act as the grizzly had and learn from the fate of others. The coyote has good judgment if he takes the time to use it.

After this experience the grizzly displayed the utmost caution in devouring animals he himself had not killed. He often found baits that had been set out for him. He investigated thoroughly and he learned that the baits near the ranch were frequently connected with traps or spring guns whereas those in the open country, where the cows passed, were always poisoned.

Little by little he grasped the reasons. He was especially alive to all clues concerning his own safety. He realized that, because of the cows, man could not set traps in the prairie, but resorted to poisoned meat. When the dogs were locked up overnight, men could afford to plant irons and spring guns on the ranch as well as poisoned baits. As long as there were live animals around, however, baits were of no use for catching the grizzly. His interest showed itself only in curiosity and in an irresistible desire to make fun of his enemies.

Roaming at night and often coming close to the ranch, Tom had noticed that the dogs were sometimes free and sometimes locked up. When he had eaten his fill and felt inclined to do mischief, he gladly paid a visit to the ranch. He learned on these excursions that there was never the twofold danger of traps and dogs in the same night. This lesson was encouraging, for he was anxious to finish off a dog.

This idea occurred to him on a winter night in the prairie when he was sniffing at the carcass of a calf which the cowboys had slit open and offered him as bait. He had already been on his way home when he scented the calf. But it was not yet dawn and he could not resist the temptation of examining the bait at close range. Immediately scenting human hands, he also imagined he smelled the mysterious poison which had played such havoc with the two coyotes. To him coyotes and dogs alike were pests, each in his own way. They were all boastful and nimble. They resembled each other so much that he confused them in his thoughts.

Somehow, the shrewd grizzly must have arrived at the conclusion that there was indeed a chance of venting the hatred which he had bottled up. Capable of putting two and two together, and with the horrid agony of the coyotes still vivid in his memory, he suddenly felt an urge to work the dogs' ruin in the same way.

The night was propitious. The wind blew so strongly in his direction that the bear could cautiously approach the houses. Obtrusive as they were by day, the dogs at night were scared of wild beasts and never ventured far from the ranch after their masters had gone to bed. The night was dark and the stars shone like luminous dots in a black sky.

Tom grumbled contentedly as he moved the calf. It would have been easy for him to carry it in his muzzle, but in the course of the winter he had become so skilled in carrying things on his back that he preferred this kind of transportation also for smaller burdens. A one-year-old calf was no test of his strength. He shoved the carcass over his shoulders and trotted to the ranch.

The distance was only a few miles and the way was straight. The bear's heavy body moved at amazing speed. It was a pleasant walk. His short legs glided in long strides over the snow.

All the time there was a head wind, but as soon as he realized that the dogs were unleashed he kept clear of the houses so as not to give his scent to the enemy too soon. He did not want to risk anything and he was not foolhardy. Moreover, he was surer of his revenge that way. The dogs would find the carcass at such a distance from the ranch that their masters could not intervene.

Everything went smoothly. The dogs, huddled in an open shed, scented Tom and gave tongue. Because of the men, the bear tried to avoid any excessive noise. He dropped the calf immediately and quickly ran back on his own trail. The wind helped him. The scent of the bear, which had alarmed the dogs, disappeared at once and, instead of it, the dogs smelled only the blood-stained calf. The carcass was worth an investigation, but there was no need to raise a big stir about it. All six dogs, three greyhounds and three fine Alsatians, raced over the snow faster than hares.

These animals, used for hunting rabbits and coyotes, were in good shape and ravenously hungry. They noticed the bear's trail but, not being bloodhounds, they refused to be disturbed by what they could not see. Their speed strengthened their self-confidence, while the smell of blood, their freedom and the darkness of night awakened their latent predatory instincts. At this moment they were rapacious animals that had lost their sense of caution through living with man. And they pounced upon the bait like wild beasts.

190

The next morning the men from the ranch found their valuable dogs dead and frozen not far off in the prairie. Perplexed, they followed the dogs' trails until they stumbled upon the remains of the calf. But the unbelievable truth dawned on them only when they saw the bear's track in the snow.

He was really no miser, the old grizzly. He had distributed generously what had been intended for him. Not for the first time he had made fools of the men, but never before had he played them such a wily trick. What he had done appeared to the men too far-fetched, too closely bordering on human cunning. A sudden little flash of thought had enabled the bear to achieve what he would not have done by relying on brute force — he had destroyed six of his deadly foes and wreaked vengeance upon the men with their own weapons. And yet there are people who say that animals cannot think!

THE BATTLE WITH MAN

by *Alden G. Stevens*

Spending time in Tanganyika as a hunter of lions led Alden G. Stevens into another kind of entertainment, that of telling lion stories. He wrote *The Way of a Lion*, from which this story is taken, and then, in 1938, *Lion Boy*, and thirteen years later, a sequel called *Lion Boy's White Brother*.

In the Serengetti region where the Carl Akeleys and the Martin Johnsons had also hunted, Alden Stevens heard of a particular kingly lion. This magnificent animal, chief actor in the following story, "because of his size and cunning . . . became a legend, a beast that savage men talked about as they sat by their fires under the African stars."

Within the thorn-brush wall of the Masai *manyatta* were crude huts of grass, and all about the village the ground was worn bare from the pressure of human feet and the scratching of chickens and the trampling of cattle. At nightfall, the cows were driven into the walls by their naked herders and spent the night there where they would be safe from marauding lions and other beasts of prey such as leopards and hyenas. The elders of the tribe and the women and children also lived within the protecting walls of thorn. Overlooking the *manyatta* was a hill and on its top was a group of huts where dwelt the *el morani*, the young warriors. From their lofty vantage point they commanded a view of the rolling plains and the village itself and ever through the days and nights their keen eyes and ears were alert for sight or sound of enemies. Like the watchmen in the towers of some old walled fortress of the middle ages, they stayed close by their weapons, and their massive shields of buffalo-hide and heavy spears could be grasped at a moment's notice if an alarm was sounded.

These savage, nomadic herdsmen, with their keen, fierce faces crowned by plastered locks of reddened hair, were a warlike folk who feared neither man nor beast. Their only food was a mixture of warm blood and milk. Their only wealth was cattle. To the protection of these half-wild, humpbacked cows they gave all that was in them of strength and cunning and knowledge. And sometimes they gave their lives when, adding to the herds through raids on the villages of neighbouring tribes, they would return victorious with stolen cattle, leaving a few of their own tribesmen dead among the burning huts of those they had despoiled.

The lean, stiff fingers of a warrior tapped rhythmically on the antelope skin head of a drum. The sound fluttered out on the night air, rising and falling like small waves. Above this primitive musician, other warriors sprawled in the light of flames that leaped scarlet-tongued from a big night-fire. The drum-beater began to chant, repeating over and over, "I saw the track of a lion today." Then as the resonant voice of the drum dropped to a faint whisper of sound, he again sang, "I saw the track of a lion today."

This constant repetition at last attracted the attention of his companions. One by one they looked at the drummer and when he saw them interested, he laid the drum on its side and sat down, saying in an ordinary tone of voice, "I saw the track of a lion today."

"We all see the tracks of lions each day we live," spoke up one of the squatting warriors. "There are many lions hereabouts."

Then a man with the slanting scars of some long-ago battle on his chest, said a bit impatiently, "Why do you keep repeating like a child, 'I saw the track of a lion today. I saw the track of a lion today' — why do you speak thus?"

"Because these tracks were large," answered the one who had drummed. "These tracks I saw were those of the largest lion that has ever walked the plains. Beside them were the tracks of another, the he-lion's mate."

There was a silence for a while as the company of warriors digested this information. "How large was this track?" asked one who had sat silently.

"As large as my two spread hands placed side by side."

Then an older warrior spoke. "Much of the game has followed the rains, even as we will do soon with our women and cattle. The many lions which were here when the game was plenty have now gone and there are but few left. The lion who leaves the big track and his mate are newcomers. Mayhap they have just arrived from a land of little meat. If so, they will be hungry and dangerous. We must tell the herd boys to watch carefully over the cattle and we too will scout the country. These lions must not kill our cows." He lapsed into silence as his companions nodded in agreement.

In spite of the extra vigilance of the Masai and the watchfulness of the little naked herd boys, each day now found a cow or a fat calf missing. Each day at sunset, some one of the terrified youngsters reported the sighting of a lion so large and savage and bold that no shouts or wavings of spears were sufficient to deter him from the grim purpose of killing. "We sit on the hilltop," related the trembling herd boys, "our cattle eating peacefully. Then, suddenly this great lion comes up from the grass close to one of our cows who has strayed a bit from the rest. He kills. Then his mate appears, coming slowly because she is heavy with unborn cubs. Together they drag the slain cow swiftly away."

When ten such stories had been heard over a period of ten days, the Masai warriors decided on a plan of action. One of the best trackers was selected to go on the morrow to the scene of the last killing and find out all possible facts about the lions that were making such bold daylight attacks on the cattle. The following night he made his report: "The big lion and his mate select a place for their killing. When a cow or calf strays a little, they kill, then drag the carcass to that place of long grass by the nearly dry water-hole at the foot of the long hill to the west of here. There they feed on the dead cow. The place stinks with the bones and flesh of our dead cattle."

There was a murmur of anger from the listening warriors. The head man spoke. "Now I will pick twenty men," he said, "and tomorrow morning, while it is yet early, we will surround this place of long grass and kill this great lion with our spears."

Thus it was agreed. The men were picked. They rubbed their

honey-brown bodies with fat, polished their seven-foot spears, saw to the stoutness of their shields. That night the drums sounded on the hilltop where the *el morani* Masai chanted the ancient song of lion-killing.

It was silent there where The Lion lay over the body of yesterday's kill. His belly was full and soon he would leave to join his lioness where she had already gone to rest among the rocks and bush of a distant ridge. The odor of decay hung about the place in the long grass where The Lion lay amidst the rotting bones and skins of the past ten days' kills. Black night turned to gray. The east paled and a flush of rose colored the horizon. In a few minutes the sun would be up. The Lion rose, yawned, and stretched mightily. Then, in an instant, he was alertly intent. He dropped swiftly to his belly, ears pricked, listening. There had been a faint sound, alien, disturbing.

For a long moment there was complete silence, then again a stealthy whispering sound as though iron caressed iron. The Lion crept forward a few feet. The morning breeze freshened, bringing the clear unmistakable odor of man to the great beast. Slowly, moving as imperceptibly as the hands of a clock, The Lion rose and peered above the grass tips.

Less than fifty feet away from him stood the glistening figure of a Masai warrior, an oval multi-colored shield covering chest and stomach, in the sinewy right hand a long shining spear that quivered and glistened in the first rays of the risen sun. Now, silently, another man stood up from the grass, stationing himself close to the first one. The Lion sank back to the shelter of the thick vegetation, turned slowly and stole away from those two figures that confronted him.

The grass moved, rustling gently with the movement of his tawny body. He had hardly gone ten feet when there was a low call, then another. Now came the roar of voices all about him. Again The Lion rose slowly and looked above the protecting grasses. Here before him were more men. A quick glance to right and left, left no further doubt in his mind. He was surrounded. A slowly narrowing circle of men was closing in on him. And as the sure knowledge of this penetrated The Lion's quick intelligence, a fierce anger touched with fear shot through him. He stood up in full view of his enemies, and as that great black-maned form met their eyes, shouts hushed and a hissing breath of awe came from them. Lions were no novelty to these primitive savages, but they had never

seen such a lion as this one, this giant whose shaggy throat blared
forth a snarling threat so full of menace that the most hardened of
these seasoned lion-hunters were daunted.

They were close to him now, moving swiftly in to kill. The Lion
saw an upraised arm, saw the gleaming thing that flew at him as the
arm shot forward. Only a lightning twist saved The Lion. The knife-

edged, rounded end of the heavy spear ripped through skin and flesh of his massive fore leg, missing the heart in that barrel chest.

What happened now was too fast for the human eyes there present to record accurately. Spears flew toward The Lion, but he was not there. As the pain of that tearing wound screamed its hot message, the beast's eye caught the form of a tall warrior among those that now rushed toward him. He charged with such sudden and deadly

speed that his onslaught broke that circle of iron and human flesh as a keen knife would rip through paper. The tall warrior went down, his spear and shield flying like grass blown by the wind, and the snapping report of his breaking neck cut short the man's screech of fear and agony. Now another spear sliced into The Lion's rear flank, but even as the strong hand that wielded it thrust the spear home, the weapon was wrenched from its grasp. The Lion's tremendous forearm flicked out and the blow tore away the man's protecting shield and laid him disemboweled on the grass.

One more spring and The Lion was free, outside the circle of his enemies. The blood of men reddened the tall grass and a trail of blood followed the fleeing beast. His flight across the plain was swift, even though impeded by the spear which rattled and clanged as he ran. The blade was clear through the rear flank, penetrating from the outside so that the tip had barely missed his lean belly. He could feel the iron grate against the leg bone as he ran. The Masai were far behind, but he was in view of them. The lioness watched his coming and joined him in flight, for he did not pause to rest. Together they went over the ridge, down to the plain on the other side. For nearly half that morning they trotted toward the northeast and at noon came to tall trees that grew by a small brown river. Here they drank, then sank exhausted to sleep.

Pain wakened The Lion. He growled, bit at the spear that protruded its short wooden haft and long iron butt from his throbbing flank. His savage voice wakened the lioness. She watched her lord a few moments, then approached him cautiously. The spear frightened her, but at last she seemed to gather her courage. Taking the heavy iron between her strong jaws, she lay back on her haunches and pulled. The spear stirred and its three-foot blade slipped from the wound. Then she licked the gaping cut for an hour or more while The Lion stretched out immovable on the sward.

Both spear wounds were deep and serious, but they mended rapidly. The two animals did not leave their resting-place for ten days except to drink. Food was scanty and they subsisted on a few rabbits, partridges and those tiny gazelles, the dik-dik, that scampered in great numbers through the dry and brittle thorn scrub. On the tenth day, the great soreness had almost entirely disappeared from lacerated flesh, and The Lion was able to travel. He and the lioness turned their heads toward the far northeast horizon and soon left the tall trees and the small brown river behind.

GREY SHADOW, THE WOLF

by Joseph Chipperfield

Into many a notebook an English boy scribbled observations on what he saw of wild animal life as he tramped the countryside near his Cornwall home. When Joseph Chipperfield grew up, these notes and other jottings in Ireland stood him in good stead as material for the fine animal stories that have made him known to a wide audience.

Chipperfield's *Beyond the Timberland Trail* is a story of three wolves. One of these, Grey Shadow, part wolf, part dog, remembers the man who cared for him. Like that other leader of a pack, in Jack London's well-known story, who felt the call of the wild, Grey Shadow, the wolf, feels the call of his heritage and has enough of a dog's nature in him to want to save his one-time friend.

Here, at a critical point, drawing a pack away from the human being they would surely assault, Grey Shadow imperils his own future leadership.

A wind was sweeping down from the barrens, a cold, freezing wind, and straight into it ran Grey Shadow, moving swiftly as if some obscure instinct warned him that if he were to save this man, who had once been his master, he would have to head off the alien pack. He skirted the outer edge of the forest, crossed the lake by going straight across the ice and loped with caution to where he knew the elk to be.

Scarcely two miles to the east came the voice of Baloo's pack. Suddenly there was no more sound to warn the elk that he had been scented, and that wolves were approaching in his direction. They were now running mute, with Baloo at their head. Their sides rose and fell with eager breathing, and their grey tails streamed out behind them.

Waiting tensely, standing betwixt them and their prey, was Grey Shadow. His head was alert and his eyes pierced the chaotic darkness as he tested the air.

Then he heard the pack, and the hair on his shoulders stiffened. First he heard the quick pattering of many feet, then across the tundra he saw the wolves themselves, dark blotches that moved swiftly across the glimmering whiteness of the snow.

Grey Shadow stood on the offensive, his hind legs firm behind him, his shoulders braced for the fight he knew must come — the fight to the death with Baloo, the timber wolf from the south.

As the pack of timber wolves approached, the first long night

of the winter ended, and the grey half-light of the shortest day
broke upon the scene. So short would the day be that before the
strange phenomena of distance had become fully revealed, the
darkness would again be descending, with perhaps the glow of the
aurora quivering far away, or perhaps a group of stars gleaming
with a metallic sharpness in a sky hard with frost.

Grey Shadow watched the marauding wolves spreading across
the tundra, their shapes oddly distorted in the grey light. They
slackened their pace as some instinct told them that Baloo, their
leader, had become suddenly apprehensive.

Baloo, ever quarrelsome when he felt his leadership threatened,
wrinkled his lips. Grey Shadow stood in the way of the kill he
considered his.

Grey Shadow moved not an inch. He just stood ready for the
attack he felt was coming.

Slowly the wolves behind Baloo began to fan out into a wide
circle — the dread circle that would gradually close in as the two
combatants fought for mastery.

A young she-wolf, Ohedeen, crept out from the grim ring, her
gaze fixed on Grey Shadow.

Out of the corner of his eye, Baloo saw her moving forward, and
with a quick lunge, he leaped on her and ripped her shoulder with
his fangs before she could jump away. It was fear of something

behind him that had prompted the attack, but in making it, he had brought himself nearer to Grey Shadow who suddenly hurled himself at the timber wolf.

His sudden attack was to Baloo's advantage. The elder animal whirled around, and his shoulders caught Grey Shadow in the side, the blow making him momentarily breathless. As he half turned to meet Baloo face to face, the timber wolf, exercising his great cunning, made an upward slash with his jaws, and gripped Grey Shadow by the shaggy fur beneath his throat.

Had the hold been a little higher, Baloo would have ripped the jugular and the fight been over. As it was, he essayed to tighten his grip, but Grey Shadow, rearing upward, half lifted Baloo, leaving his stomach unprotected. With a swift wriggling movement, the younger animal at the risk of falling beneath his opponent, dug him with his hind legs, and with a growl, Baloo loosened his hold and found himself facing an animal more powerful than himself and far more agile.

Grey Shadow stood with ears aslant, and fangs gleaming. Baloo's body went low to the ground, prior to making a leap. His posture

was typical of the wolf, while that of Grey Shadow was more of the dog.

Then Baloo made the leap. In a flash, Grey Shadow moved a little to the left, and Baloo fell heavily in the snow. He stumbled badly, and before he could regain his feet, Grey Shadow was astride his back, his fangs sinking deep into Baloo's neck.

The timber wolf roared with pain, and attempted to roll over. Grey Shadow had been prepared for such a move and immediately released his hold, with the result that Baloo lay on his back with his throat unprotected.

For one short instant he lay thus, one short instant that cost him his life. Quickly Grey Shadow gripped his opponent's throat, and held on.

The ring of waiting wolves had narrowed; one and all were ready to rush in and rend the defeated leader.

When Grey Shadow became aware that Baloo's body had gone limp beneath him, he sprang away, and the slain leader's pack did the rest. In a hungry, undisciplined horde, they rent the large timber wolf who had led them so long, and did not cease mutilation of his body until they heard, issuing from Grey Shadow's throat, the cry of primitive victory!

As they slunk away from what was left of Baloo, they saw Grey Shadow squatting on his haunches. Standing beside him was Ohe-deen, and they knew that from henceforward he was her chosen mate.

Immediately the wolves had overcome the excitement of the kill, they began to cast furtive glances at Grey Shadow whom now they expected to assume the leadership. Whenever an old leader had been overthrown, past experience told them that the new leader, to show complete superiority and mastery over the pack, instantly took his place at its head and set off for new and profitable hunting grounds.

Grey Shadow was aware of this long-standing tradition. He knew, too, that if he led the pack on the trail of the elk Baloo had been hunting down, there was every possibility that the camp in the spruce forest would be invaded, if not by the entire pack, then by one or two isolated members when they disbanded.

At the back of Grey Shadow's mind, this fact was a strange, recurring fear. His reason for attacking Baloo had been due to his great desire to keep the pack in a northerly direction, instead of travelling southwest.

The wolves meanwhile became restive. Each member was thin-ribbed and obviously starving, so different from the pack Grey Shadow usually led.

Suddenly, in the wind that had swept down from the tundra, Grey Shadow scented meat. He stood up — Ohedeen watching him with eagerness. Her desire to go wherever he went was expressed in every line of her slim, young body. She sniffed his shoulders, and as he turned his head, her tongue lightly flicked his nose.

He was about to respond when again the scent of meat tickled his nostrils. Instinct told him that the warm smell of flesh was of moose, and that the herd was travelling a little to the northeast.

He was undecided as to what he should do. He could not forget the man who lay under the rude coverings before a dying campfire. The vision of that man was strong before him. There was, moreover, a curious gentleness welling up inside him, making him soft when he should be strong. Had any member of the pack challenged him then, Grey Shadow would have found it difficult to hold his own. Even the glow in his eyes had changed. The look of a dog was in them.

Just then, a lean, bristling wolf moved a little to the fore, standing

apart from his fellows. The challenge he was about to give was never uttered.

Grey Shadow whined in his throat and faced the direction from which the wind was blowing. Then, shaking off the disturbing influence of the dog Klaus, who had been his sire, he began to lope forward with the easy questing gait of his kind, Ohedeen running at his side.

In ones and twos, the wolves began to form behind him, and in less than ten minutes, the grey legion was travelling rapidly down a slope that ended in a small hollow where three yearling calves were facing the wind. They had been endeavouring for the past few days to join up with the main herd that had passed over the flank of the ice hummock, and had become the centre of the attack made by Grey Shadow's pack, led by Broken Fang.

So silently did the timber wolves descend the hollow that they had already fanned out into horseshoe formation before the calves realized they were to be the victims.

207

Grey Shadow, with Ohedeen close at his heels, leaped for the throat of the nearest beast. So swift was he that he had a firm hold before the creature could defend himself.

Ohedeen, having jumped short of her objective, swung round, and with a quick, upward snap of her jaws, made for the animal's flank. With a snort of fear, the hapless yearling sagged to one side, becoming in an instant completely hamstrung.

The remaining two calves galloped away, with part of the pack in pursuit. Those travelling close on Grey Shadow's rear aided him in bringing down his own selected prey.

Scarcely five minutes had passed since the attack when the trampled, blood-reddened snow told its own tale. As Grey Shadow sent his triumphant call sounding across the frozen wastes, those of the pack who had assisted him in the kill set about gorging themselves.

Grey Shadow himself ate but little. He kept continually staring toward the southwest.

Again he felt the urge to return, and although once more he pointed his nose to the skies and sent his call echoing over the snow, there was a different sound in it. No wolf of the northern packs had ever called thus before. The note, beginning low, swelled into a weird lament as he mourned for that which he had lost.

After he had ceased to unburden his heart of the great unrest that was in it, Grey Shadow began to edge away from his companions. When some twenty yards away, he stopped and glanced back. The wolves were still eating, stopping only for a moment when another of the pack gave forth the call of triumph — the sound coming from two miles away in the direction taken by the other two yearlings.

Then Grey Shadow began to run swiftly due southwest, travelling with the wind. Unknown to him, less than thirty yards in the rear came Ohedeen, intent on keeping in sight the one she was pleased to recognize as her mate.

JIM'S CIRCUS CROCODILE

by Sir Percy Fitzpatrick

The incident related here is recorded by Sir Percy Fitzpatrick in his exciting life of his famous dog. *Jock of the Bushveld* has for more than fifty years introduced people to the marvellous wild life of the South Africa Bushveld. The crocodile is one of the most feared of animals, and, he says, the only one that is hated.

There is nothing that one comes across in hunting more horrible and loathsome than the crocodile: nothing that rouses the feeling of horror and hatred as it does: nothing that so surely and quickly gives the sensation of "creeps in the back" as the noiseless apparition of one in the water just where you least expected anything, or the discovery of one silently and intently watching you with its head resting flat on a sand-spit — the thing you had seen half a dozen times before and mistaken for a small rock. Many things are hunted in the Bushveld; but only the crocodile is hated. There is always the feeling of horror that this hideous, cowardly cruel thing — the enemy of man and beast alike — with its look of a cunning smile in the greeny glassy eyes and great wide mouth, will mercilessly drag you down — down — down to the bottom of some deep still pool, and hold you there till you drown. Utterly helpless yourself to escape or fight, you cannot even call, and if you could, no one could help you there. It is all done in silence: a few bubbles come up where a man went down; and that is the end of it.

We all knew about the crocodiles and were prepared for them, but the sport was good, and when you are fresh at the game and get interested in a hunt it is not very easy to remember all the things you have been warned about and the precautions you were told to take. It was on the first day at the river that one of our party, who was not a very old hand at hunting, came in wet and muddy and told us how a crocodile had scared the wits out of him. He had gone out after guinea-fowl, he said, but as he had no dog to send in and flush them, the birds simply played with him: they would not rise but kept running in the reeds a little way in front of him, just out of sight. He could hear them quite distinctly, and thinking to steal a march on them took off his boots and got on to the rocks.

Stepping bare-footed from rock to rock where the reeds were thin, he made no noise at all and got so close up that he could hear the little whispered chink-chink-chink that they give when near danger. The only chance of getting a shot at them was to mount one of the big rocks from which he could see down into the reeds; and he worked his way along a mud-bank towards one. A couple more steps from the mud-bank on to a low black rock would take him to the big one. Without taking his eyes off the reeds where the guinea-fowl were he stepped cautiously on to the low black rock, and in an instant was swept off his feet, tossed and tumbled over and over, into the mud and reeds, and there was a noise of furious rushing and crashing as if a troop of elephants were stampeding through the reeds. He had stepped on the back of a sleeping crocodile; no doubt it was every bit as frightened as he was. There was much laughter over this and the breathless earnestness with which he told the story; but there was also a good deal of chaff, for it seems to be generally accepted that you are not bound to believe all hunting stories; and Jim and his circus crocodile became the joke of the camp.

TARKA'S JOYFUL WATER-LIFE

by Henry Williamson

Even though there is in it an occasional reference not a part of the daily talk of city-bred readers — the word for a little wooded clump, *holt*, for instance — Henry L. Williamson's story of *Tarka the Otter* is one of the finest in the literature of animal life. It won the author the Hawthornden Prize in 1927 and proved to be the turning point in his career as a writer.

Here Tarka's mother initiates him into fishing.

One warm evening when the river was low, the mother swam down to the holt and called the cubs into the water, and although they were ravening, she did not climb up, but waited for them with a fish below the tree. They whimpered and peered, moving their heads sideways and telling her that below was fearful. She lay on her back in the water and let the fish go, in order to catch it, and rise with it gleaming again. The two youngest cubs ran back over the damp, trodden couch to get through the tunnel, but they were too fat to squeeze through. Perhaps Tarka would have gone with them, if he had not wanted the fish so much. His eyes were on it, he smelled it, his mouth filled with eat-water. He mewed, he yikkered, he tissed, but there was no fish. The otter swam on her back and called him into the water.

Tarka watched her. He wanted the fish, but he dared not let go with his feet. The fish came no nearer, so he dropped down into the black, star-shivery water. He was clutched in a cold and terrible embrace, so that he could neither see nor breathe, and although he tried to walk, it smothered him, choked him, roared in his ears, and stifled every mew for help, until his mother swam under him, pressing pads and tail against his back. Tarka was carried to the stony margin of an islet, where the closed flowers of the water-crowsfoot were floating among their leaves. He spluttered and sneezed and shook water out of his eyes, and saw the stars above him, and felt his mother's tongue on his head.

Once while swimming in his happy way, he noticed the moon. It danced on the water just before his nose. Often he had seen the moon, just outside the hollow tree, and had tried to touch it with a paw. Now he tried to bite it, but it swam away from him. He chased it. It wriggled like a silver fish and he followed to the sedges on the far bank of the river, but it no longer wriggled. It was waiting to play with him. Across the river Tarka could hear the mewing of his sisters, but he set off after the moon over the meadow. He ran among buttercups and cuckoo-flowers and grasses bending with bright points. Farther and farther from the river he ran, the moonlight gleaming on his coat. Really it was brown like the dust in an October puff-ball, but the water sleeked the hair.

As he stopped to listen to the bleat of lambs, a moth whirred by his head and tickled him. While he was scratching, a bird flying with irregular wingbeats and sudden hawk-like glidings took the moth in its wide gape and flew out of his sight. Tarka forgot the moon-play. He crouched in the grasses, which rose above his head like the trees of a forest, some with tops like his rudder, others like his whiskers, and all whispering as they swayed. The nightjar returned, clapping its wings over its head with the noise of a dry stick cracking. Tarka was glad to hear his mother calling him. He mewed. He listened and her whistle was nearer, so he ran away in the wet grasses. The cub did not know how alarmed his mother was nor did he know that less than fifty flaps away a bird with great eyes and wings spanning a yard was flying upon him. The nightjar had seen the bird, too, and had clapped its wings as a danger signal to its mate whose two eggs were laid among ferns in the wood.

The nightjar twirled and planed away; Tarka scampered on. The great bird, who had raised two tufts of feathers on its head, dropped with taloned feet spread for a clutch. The otter saw it drop and ran forwards so swiftly that the sound of her going through the grasses was like the first wind which uncoils as it runs before the southwesterly gale. The bird, which was a short-eared owl, thought that Tarka was a small rabbit, and fanned above him while it considered whether or not he was small enough to be attacked. It did not hesitate longer than the time of six flaps, but stopped, while screaking to terrify and subdue its prey. But Tarka came of a family fiercer and quicker in movement than the owl. Tissing with rage, he jumped and bit his assailant as a foot grasped his back and four talons pierced his skin. The other foot of the bird grasped grasses and it had turned with clacking beak to peck the base of the cub's skull when the paw-stroke of the bitch tore half the feathers from its breast. She stood on it, bit once, twice, thrice, in a second of time, and so the owl died.

213

Tarka was nipped in the neck, shaken, picked up, bumped all the way back to the bank, scraped over the stones, and dropped into the water. Obediently he followed his mother across the river.

On a November evening, when the ebb-tide was leaning the channel buoys to the west and the gulls were flying silent and low over the sea to the darkening cliffs of the headland, Tarka and his much older friend, Greymuzzle, set out on a journey. They had followed the salmon up the river, and Greymuzzle had returned for a purpose. The bright eye of the lighthouse, standing like a bleached bone at the edge of the sandhills, blinked in the clear air. The otters were carried down amidst swirls and topplings of waves in the wake of a ketch, while the mumble of the bar grew in their ears. Beyond the ragged horizon of grey breakers the day had gone, clouded and dull, leaving a purplish pallor on the cold sea.

The waves slid and rose under the masted ship, pushing the white surge of the bar from her bows. A crest rolled under her keel and she pitched into a trough. On the left a mist arose off a bank of grey boulders, on which a destroyer lay broken and sea-scattered. It had lain there for years, in bits like beetle fragments in a gorse-spider's grey web-tunnel. One of the great seas that drive the flying spume over the potwallopers' grazing marsh had thrown it up on the Pebble Ridge. During the day Tarka and Greymuzzle had slept under the rusty plates, curled warm on the wave-worn boulders rolled there by the seas along Hercules Promontory.

Two hours after midnight the otters had swum five miles along the shallow coast and had reached the cave of the headland, which Greymuzzle had remembered when she had felt her young kick inside her. The tide left deep pools among the rocks, which the otters searched for blennies and gobies, and other little fish which lurked under the seaweed. They caught prawns, which were eaten tail first, but the heads were never swallowed. With their teeth they tore mussels off the rocks, and holding them in their paws, they cracked them and licked out the fish. While Greymuzzle was digging out a sand-eel, Tarka explored a deep pool where dwelt a one-clawed lobster. It was hiding two yards under a rock, at the end of a cleft too narrow to swim up. Four times he tried to hook it out with his fore-pad, the claws of which were worn down with sand-scratching, and in his eagerness to get at it he tore seaweed with his teeth. The lobster had been disturbed many times in its life, for nearly every man of the villages of Cryde and Ham had tried to dislodge it with long sticks to which they had lashed hooks. The lobster had lost so many claws that, after nine had been wrenched off, its brain refused to grow any more.

215

The otters rested by day on a ledge in the cave under the headland. Here dwelt Jaark the seal, who climbed a slab below them by shuffles and flapping jumps. Sometimes Tarka swam in the pools of the cave, rolling on his back to bite the drops of ironwater which dripped from the rocky roof, but only when Jaark was away in the sea, hunting the conger where the rocks of Bag Leap ripped foam out of the tide.

The greatest conger of Bag Leap, who was Garbargee, had never been caught, for whenever it saw Jaark the seal, its enemy, it hid far down in the crab-green water, in a hole in the rocks of the deepest pool, where lay shell-crusted cannon and gear of H. M. sloop *Weazel* wrecked there a century before. When no seal was about, Garbargee hung out of the hole and stared, unblinkingly, for fish, which it pursued and swallowed.

One morning as Tarka, hungry after a stormy night, was searching in the thong-weed five fathoms under the glimmering surface, something flashed above him, and looking up, he saw a narrow head with a long hooked preying beak and two large webs ready to thrust in chase of fish. This was Oylegrin the shag, whose oily greenish-black feathers reflected light. The smooth narrow head flickered as Oylegrin shifted his gaze, and a pollack below mistook the flicker for a smaller surface-swimming fish. The pollack turned to rise and take it, and the shag saw the gleam of its side at the same time as Tarka saw it. Oylegrin tipped up and kicked rapidly downwards, faster than an otter could swim. Its tight feathers glinted and gleamed as it pursued the pollack. Garbargee also saw the pollack and uncurled a muscular tail from its hold on a jut of rock. The conger was longer than a man is tall, and thicker through the body than Tarka. It weighed ninety pounds. It waved about the weedy timbers, and as it passed over, crabs hid in the mouths of cannon.

Bird, animal, and fish made a chasing arrow-head whose tip was the glinting pollack; conger the flexible shaft, otter and shag the barbs. Oylegrin swam with long neck stretched out, hooked beak ready to grip, while he thrust with webbed feet farther from the bubbles which ran out of his gullet. The pollack turned near Tarka, who swung up and followed it. Oylegrin braked and swerved with fourteen short stiff tail-feathers and one upturned web. The pollack turned down a sheer rock hung with thong-weed, but, meeting Tarka, turned up again and was caught by Oylegrin.

The chasing arrow-head buckled against the rock, in a tangle of thongs and ribbons and bubbles shaking upwards. The giant conger had bitten the shag through the neck. Wings flapped, a grating, muffled cry broke out of a bottle of air. Tarka's mouth opened wide, but his teeth could not pierce the conger's skin. The gloom darkened, for an opaqueness was spreading where there had been movement.

Now Jaark the seal, who had been searching round the base of the rock, saw an otter rising to the surface, and was swinging up towards him when he saw a conger eel wave out the opaqueness,

which was Oylegrin's blood staining the green gloom. Garbargee held the shag in its jaws. The undersea cloud was scattered by the swirls of flippers as the seal chased the conger. Garbargee dropped the shag, and the cleft of rock received its grey tenant. Jaark swung up with a bend of his smooth body, and lay under the surface with only his head out, drinking fresh air, and looking at Tarka six yards away. *Wuff, wuff,* said Jaark, playfully. *Iss, Iss,* cried Tarka in alarm. The pollack escaped, and soon afterwards was feeding with other fish on the crab-nibbled corpse of the shag.

FOXES AT PLAY

by W. H. Hudson

W. H. Hudson is one of the great writers among naturalists. He was born of American parents in 1841 in the Argentine. There he spent his first thirty-three years before making his home in England where he lived, roaming the countryside recording all that he saw and heard in his many books, until he died in 1922. From one of his best known books, *A Shepherd's Life*, of which the principal character is Shepherd Caleb Bawcombe, come these charming descriptions of foxes.

When speaking of foxes Caleb always maintained that in his part of the country there were two sorts: one small and very red, the larger one of a lighter colour with some grey in it. And it is possible that the hill foxes differed somewhat in size and colour from those of the lower country. He related that one year two vixens littered at one spot, a deep bottom among the downs, so near together that when the cubs were big enough to come out they mixed and played in company; the vixens happened to be of the different sorts, and the difference in colour appeared in the little ones as well.

Caleb was so taken with the pretty sight of all these little foxes, neighbours and playmates, that he went evening after evening to sit for an hour or longer watching them. One thing he witnessed which will perhaps be disbelieved by those who have not closely observed animals for themselves, and who still hold to the fable that all wild creatures are born with an inherited and instinctive knowledge and dread of their enemies. Rabbits swarmed at that spot, and he observed that when the old foxes were not about the young, half-grown rabbits would freely mix and play with the little foxes. He was so surprised at this, never having heard of such a thing, that he told his master of it, and the farmer went with him on a moonlight night and the two sat for a long time together, and saw rabbits and foxes playing, pursuing one another round and round, the rabbits when pursued often turning very suddenly and jumping clean over their pursuer.

In Berkshire I once met with that rare being, an intelligent game-keeper who took an interest in wild animals, and knew from obser-vation a great deal about their habits. During an after-supper talk, kept up till past midnight, we discussed the subject of strange, erratic actions in animals, which in some cases appear contrary to their own natures. He gave an instance of such behaviour in a fox that had its earth at a spot on the border of a wood where rabbits were abundant. One evening he was at this spot, standing among the trees and watching a number of rabbits feeding and gambolling on the green turf, when the fox came trotting by and the rabbits paid no attention. Suddenly he stopped and made a dart at a rabbit; the rabbit ran from him a distance of twenty to thirty yards, then suddenly turning round went for the fox and chased it back some distance, after which the fox again chased the rabbit, and so they went on, turn and turn about, half a dozen times. It was evident, he said, that the fox had no wish to catch and kill a rabbit, that it was nothing but play on his part, and that the rabbits responded in the same spirit, knowing that there was nothing to fear.

Another instance of this playful spirit of the fox with an enemy, which I heard recently, is of a gentleman who was out with his

221

dog, a fox-terrier, for an evening walk in some woods near his house. On his way back he discovered on coming out of the woods that a fox was following him, at a distance of about forty yards. When he stood still the fox sat down and watched the dog. The dog appeared indifferent to its presence until his master ordered him to go for the fox, whereupon he charged him and drove him back to the edge of the wood, but at that point the fox turned and chased the dog right back to its master, then once more sat down and appeared very much at his ease. Again the dog was encouraged to go for him and hunted him again back to the wood, and was then in turn chased back to its master. After several repetitions of this performance, the gentleman went home, the fox still following, and on going in closed the gate behind him, leaving the fox outside, sitting in the road as if waiting for him to come out again to have some more fun.

This incident serves to remind me of an experience I had one evening in King's Copse, an immense wood of oak and pine in the New Forest near Exbury. It was growing dark when I heard on or close to the ground, some twenty to thirty yards before me, a low, wailing cry, resembling the hunger-cry of the young, long-eared owl. I began cautiously advancing, trying to see it, but as I advanced the cry receded, as if the bird was flitting from me. Now, just after I had begun following the sound a fox uttered his sudden, startlingly loud scream about forty yards away on my right hand, and the next moment a second fox screamed on my left, and from that time I was accompanied, or shadowed, by the two foxes, always keeping abreast of me, always at the same distance, one screaming and the other replying about every half-minute. The distressful bird-sound ceased, and I turned and went off in another direction, to get out of the wood on the side nearest the place where I was staying, the foxes keeping with me until I was out.

What moved them to act in such a way is a mystery, but it was perhaps play to them.

Another curious instance of foxes playing was related to me by a gentleman at the little village of Inkpen, near the Beacon, in Berkshire. He told me that when it happened, a good many years ago, he sent an account of it to the *Field*. His gamekeeper took him one day "to see a strange thing," to a spot in the woods where a fox had a litter of four cubs, near a long, smooth, green slope. A little distance from the edge of the slope three round swedes were lying on the turf. "How do you think these swedes came here?" said the keeper, and then proceeded to say that the old fox must have brought them there from the field a long distance away, for her cubs to play with. He had watched them of an evening, and wanted his master to come and see too. Accordingly they went in the evening, and hiding themselves among the bushes near, waited till the young foxes came out and began rolling the swedes about and jumping at and tumbling over them. By and by one rolled down the slope, and the young foxes went after it all the way down, and then, when they had worried it sufficiently, they returned to the top and played with another swede until that was rolled down, then with the third one in the same way. Every morning, the keeper said, the swedes were found back on top of the ground, and he had no doubt that they were taken up by the old fox again and left there for her cubs to play with.

SOMETHING TO GROUSE ABOUT

by Hans Fallada

Hans Fallada, the best-selling German novelist who wrote *Little Man, What Now?*, wrote one children's story: a charming book for his daughter Midge about a badger who lived near their home. It was discovered after his death and published in several countries. In English it appeared as *That Rascal, Fridolin.*

At the time when Fridolin drove his mother out of the set he was a handsome, well-set-up young fellow with a thick layer of fat under his coat and a round paunch almost touching the ground. Any badger girl would have wagged her tail with pleasure at the sight of him.

Tight, bristle-like hair, glossy and fairly long, covered his whole body, including his ears. On his back he was a whitey-grey mixed with black, towards the side and tail he was more of a reddish colour, but on the underside and paws he was a blackish-brown. His head was white. On either side of his snout ran a black stripe, broadening as it rose above his eyes and white ears and losing itself on his neck. He measured two and a half feet from the tip of the snout to the root of the tail, but his neat little brush made another eight inches. He was no taller than a school ruler, a mere foot. Now, in the autumn and feeding well, he weighed thirty-eight pounds. Taking him all in all he was a fine, good-looking animal.

With the first onset of frost he curled up in his set, head between forepaws, and fell into a deep sleep. Through winter storms, snow and ice he slept on; and still peacefully sleeping he lay there while the ground crackled with frost, feeding all the while on his own fat. But deep down in his dark sleeping-place, he sensed any mild sunny days as they came. Then he woke up, sneezed once or twice, and slowly padded through the tunnel towards the daylight, scenting warily to make sure the coast was clear. Then he ambled down to the lake, took a deep drink, did his little business, and covered the droppings carefully so that nothing should be left to betray his presence. Now he climbed back to his set, lay for a while lazily in the sun and licked his coat clean. At length he made his way into his den, munched a few carrots and beechnuts and continued his winter sleep.

This was his life until the warmer weather came. Only when the grass had turned green and the trees began to shoot was there plenty of food about — and not before time, for he had used up the last ounce of fat in his body. He was as thin as a rake and there was no sign now of a nice little paunch. Not a single badger girl would have looked at him with pleasure, particularly as his coat had lost its gloss.

Fridolin now lived just as he had done the year before with his mother Friedebel except that he slept alone, basked alone in the sun, and hunted alone. He enjoyed things much better that way. He always had peace now and the softest place in the den; and of course all the tender morsels were his. With such a life he soon became nice and round again and his coat took on a new sheen.

He had long since forgotten his mother's warning words, but he was by nature cautious. All the same, for a badger, he was enterprising. Liking good food, he often visited the garden where Asta, the dog, had once so terrified him. The farmer's wife was very vexed when her new carrots and peas disappeared, but she had no idea who the thief could be. Many animals were suspected, but never a badger, for none had ever been seen on the Hullerbusch farm.

On one of his nightly forages Fridolin saw his mother again. He was sniffing a rotten tree-stump for worms and beetles when she passed close by, so close that the two almost touched. The son just looked up for a moment from his tasty meal, then lowered his snout back into the stump and went on contentedly chewing. Mother ran on without a sound either. They didn't even wish each other "Good hunting". That's the way with animals when the children have once left their mother. They become strangers, don't even recognise each other, and never dream of going to each other's help.

Now Fridolin might have gone on for many years leading this quiet, solitary existence in the set on the lake-bank if the forester's little fox Reynard hadn't slipped his chain.

Unused to fending for himself, Reynard was very tired and hungry when he came to Fridolin's wood many days later.

It took Reynard three days to cover the whole of the Hullerbusch, but by that time he really knew it down to the last ant-heap. After all, this beautiful beechwood was not large, the length being less than half an hour's walk and the breadth less than a quarter's. It was exactly the place Reynard had been looking for — there wasn't another fox, people were seldom about, and food was abundant.

The main thing was to find a home quickly, as he was tired of sleeping under bushes and in shabby rabbit-holes. He must have a real earth with a number of bolt-holes in case some day he happened to be chased by dogs or men. He could well have dug a hole — he had the claws to do so — but no mother had taught him how and in any case he was much too weak and lazy. He had found three holes in the Hullerbusch and with his usual impudence he took it that he had only to choose the one he wanted and help himself. The first was Fridolin's sister Friederika's set on the open bank towards the fields, and this he at once turned down for the very reason Mother Friedebel had given — it was risky because too exposed. The second was the old foxhole Friedebel now lived in, and he rejected it because it smelt too damp and fusty.

The remaining one was the fine hole under the thin belt of beeches on the south slope to the Lower Lake — Fridolin's. It was this hole on which Reynard cast a covetous eye, but he couldn't seize this very desirable residence by force while he was weak and tired. More than once during his exploring trips he had spied the badger basking comfortably in the sun. He had observed the strong, well-fed body and admired the powerful teeth, but because he was in better heart now that he had left the big forest, they didn't frighten him. He was sure that here in the Hullerbusch all would be easy for him, and that went for an earth too, since he fully expected the badger to welcome him into his home as a friend.

A first attempt to make friends with Fridolin didn't come off, however. One fine summer's afternoon the badger was lying snugly on his back in the sun, warming his paunch and grunting contentedly, when Reynard came padding along ever so softly, his lean belly sweeping the dust. He pushed his way quite close to the badger and

began sunning himself alongside him. The badger lay on his back, the fox on his stomach, one drowsily content, the other wary with eyes blinking craftily.

Rudely awakened from the happiest of dreams, Fridolin lay for a while stock-still with astonishment. Then he cast a few side-glances at the newcomer. He hadn't seen a fox before, but this animal looked a bit like the hated dogs, and its scent increasingly offended his sensitive nostrils. It was a scent he loathed and rightly called "a stink".

Fridolin was normally a lazy fellow with a slow brain, but the stink made him think a lot faster. All of a sudden he turned over on his side and gave the fox a good taste of his teeth, making him spring up and retreat into the thicket, howling and yelping. Furious at the inroad on his hermit life, Fridolin crept into his dark set and began drowsily thinking over the drawbacks of this world when even the best of badgers can't be left to sun his belly in peace.

It took a couple of days before Reynard would trust himself near the vicious hermit again, and this time he went about things more cunningly. He lay meekly down in the dust, flat on his stomach, a little distance from the badger, and held out a special gift for him in his jaws. It was a big ringsnake, and had been very hard to part with as he badly wanted it to satisfy his own keen hunger.

Fridolin blinked once. He blinked twice. A fat ring-snake a yard long makes a capital dinner. The fox pushed closer, still on his

stomach and more and more humble in manner, till at length he
spat the snake out at the badger's feet. Fridolin at once snatched it
up and gladly ate it. Now squatting on his haunches and intently
watching, Reynard wagged his brush from right to left and from
left to right, with every sign of goodwill. He followed each bite,
eyes greedy with envy, as the food passed from the mouth through
the throat to the stomach, while the saliva dribbled from his own
jaws with desire.

As soon as the badger had finished eating, the fox made up to
him afresh, but again Fridolin snapped at him fiercely. The fox got
a fright and leapt into the air with all four legs, then ran away as
fast as he could. Again Fridolin went into his set and wondered
wearily if these disturbances would ever cease.

Being meek and polite, even giving a nice present, had made no
difference with the crabby hermit. Any creature but a fox would
have given up all hope. Fox, however, is always fox even if brought
up on a milk-bottle at a forester's ten times over, and he, Reynard,
still had another trick up his sleeve. This was a far better one than
to employ soft soap; it was to try impudence.

That night he spied on the badger from behind a broad beech-
trunk to see when he would quit his set to go foraging, leaving the
coast clear. Even then it was a long time before the clumsy chap
was well out of the way, and Reynard grinned to himself to see
him laboriously turning over every stone and every scrap of bark

in the hope of a find. The time Fridolin took to cover a hundred yards would have been enough for the quick Reynard to run all round the Hullerbusch.

No sooner had the badger completely gone than Reynard slunk into the set. He found it even better than he expected. The tunnels were all that one could wish, and the den, padded with bracken, moss and long grasses, could be called really smart. But one thing about the otherwise delightful set failed to please him: it had no stench. It just smelt like fresh air — like absolutely nothing! And it was almost indecently clean.

In a real foxhole you could cut the air with a knife, such a nice ripe smell it would have of rotten game, carrion, decaying meat and dung. You would know where you were: not outside in the forest but snug at home among foxes. From the topmost entrance to the hole you ought to smell who was living down below. How nice this set would have been if the tunnels had been adorned a bit with old, damp chicken feathers or a rotting bone sticking out here and there, or if there'd been some dung about — then it would have been a true fox paradise!

From word to deed was but one step and Reynard lifted his brush, curved his back cat-fashion and deposited a goodly heap of droppings right in the midst of the badger's cosy bed. It was his visiting card he was leaving.

So on his return from the night's foraging Fridolin got a nasty shock. He sniffed something wrong the moment he entered the set. He pushed on deeper into the tunnel, drawing more and more unwilling breaths, and when he came to his den he all but fainted with the smell. He could guess who the culprit was who had popped this greeting plumb in the centre of his bed. But what good did it do him to know? And what good would it be if the villain himself were there? Even if he killed Reynard it wouldn't take away the stink that was poisoning the whole place!

At first Fridolin was quite at a loss to know how he could get rid of the heap of filth, since he couldn't possibly bring himself to touch it. At length it occurred to him that he might dig a trench round it, undermine it till all had fallen into the pit, then cover it over firmly with soil.

But with the removal of the dung the stench had by no means gone and Fridolin had to make up his mind to sleep outside. A steady drip from the beech leaves forced him to keep shifting his

229

place and he could not find a really dry one. A quiet, comfortable sleep was out of the question. Like the whole tribe of badgers Fridolin was an awkward fellow, on the defensive against everybody and everything, and this affair made him much more so. He hated the whole world.

Meanwhile the fox, hidden behind the beech-trunk, had watched the going-in and coming-out-again of the badger and how, despite the wet, he had tried to sleep in the open. Reynard felt sure he was now on the right track. So from that day onwards Fridolin hadn't one quiet moment and his home became a place of torment. Each day he would do out his sleeping-place with soft new padding, cleaning and airing it well, then tired with all the work he would lie down to sleep. But it would be only a little while before he was wakened by the horrible stench of another visiting-card left by the fox, who crept in stealthily by one of the bolt-holes. Then the work would have to start all over again.

This made Fridolin turn even more bitter against the world; even his health began to fail. His nice round paunch faded away and nothing remained of the layer of fat under his coat, which was glossy no longer. But Reynard became stronger and stronger; he had to be on the go all the time — otherwise he couldn't have kept his stomach full and provided constant new heaps for the badger's den. His green eyes had a jaunty look, his fur gleamed red as a flame, and he carried his brush high in an arch of triumph. All the timidity that had made him humble when he was in the forester's house and in the great forest had vanished. He looked on the Huller-busch as his and felt a king.

Fridolin was far too lazy and sluggish for it to occur to him that he might corner the crafty fox and meet him in open fight. He never

230

saw Reynard again, for the struggle was over. One night when he got back to find the set fouled, this time in three or four places and worse than ever, he just rushed out again into the pure night air and gave up all idea of another futile clean-up. The fox had won the day. He had stunk the badger out!

Fridolin sat down before the entrance to his set and cursed this sorry world where the peaceful are at the mercy of the wicked. It never entered his head that what had been done to him was only what he had done to his own mother. He had been turned out of the same set from which he had ungratefully driven her. This simply didn't occur to him. He was disappointed with the world: a detestable place. He pined for some spot where there would be no dogs, no men and, above all, no foxes; only little creatures, who wouldn't bother him but would be eatable. Though still on this earth, Fridolin yearned for the badgers' heaven.

He could easily have gone farther into the Hullerbusch and pushed his mother out of her old foxhole, but he was disgusted with the wood which had delighted him until he was forced to share it with the loathsome fox.

His mind was now made up to leave his native wood and go out into the wide world to try his luck. Surely he would find the badgers' paradise somewhere. Or so Fridolin thought.

A JUNGLE DETECTIVE STORY

by Jim Corbett

Lt.-Col. Corbett was born and bred in the high Kumaon hills in India and there he learnt his tremendous skill with animals and love of wild life. He became so experienced a naturalist and so skilled in jungle craft that his power to interpret and imitate the noises of beast and bird was sharp enough to deceive even the tiger. He wrote several exciting books based on his experiences and especially his struggles with man-eating tigers, for he was much in demand wherever an injured animal turned to human prey and terrorized the country. This story comes from *Jungle Lore*. After the Second World War he settled in Kenya where he died in 1955.

Detective stories of fiction usually start with the evidence of some violent crime or attempted crime, and the enthralled reader — oblivious for the time being that he is reading fiction — is carried along through exciting scene after scene until finally the criminal is detected and made to suffer for his crime. My jungle detective stories do not start in the same way, nor do they always end with punishment for the criminal. I will select at random one of these stories from memory's library.

The forest road beside which I had camped was little used by human beings and as there was an abundance of game in the forest through which it ran, an early morning walk along it was of great interest, for on the road, which was of hard clay with a light film of dust on it, was a record of all the animals that had used or crossed it during the night. When looking at tracks on a road or game path, with a trained eye, it is not necessary to stop at each track to determine the species, size, movement, and so on of the animal or animals that have made the track, for these details are subconsciously noted. For instance, the porcupine that had come out on to the road, a little beyond where I joined the road after leaving my camp, had evidently taken fright at something in the jungle on the right of the road and had scurried back. The reason for his fright was apparent a few yards farther on, where a bear had crossed the road from right to left. On entering the jungle on the left the bear had disturbed a sounder of pig and a small herd of cheetal, for they had dashed across the road into the jungle on the right. A little farther on, a sambhar stag had come out from the right and after browsing on a bush had walked along the road for fifty yards, rubbed his antlers against a young sapling, and then gone back into the jungle. Near this spot a four-horned antelope, with a fawn at foot, had come on the road. The fawn, whose hoof-prints were no bigger than the finger nails of a child, had skipped about the road until the mother had taken fright, and after dashing down the road for a few yards mother and fawn had gone into the jungle. Here there was a bend in the road, and at the bend were the footprints of a hyaena who had come as far as this, and then turned and gone back the way it had come.

Reading the signs on the road and listening to the birds — Sandni Gaga in addition to being the most beautiful spot for a hundred miles round is noted for its bird life — I had covered half a mile when I came to a stretch of the road that had been cut out of the face of the hill. Here the surface was too hard to show normal

tracks and I had gone a short distance along the road when my attention was arrested by an unusual mark. This was a little furrow three inches long and two inches deep where it started, and it was at right angles to the road. The furrow could have been made by a staff with an iron point, but no human being had been along the road for twenty-four hours and the furrow had been made within the past twelve hours. And again, if a human being had made it it would have been parallel with and not at right angles to the road, which at this point was fourteen feet wide with a more or less perpendicular bank some ten feet high on the right and a steep slope on the left. The earth thrown out of the furrow showed that the object that had made it had travelled from right to left.

Having satisfied myself that the furrow had not been made by a human being, I came to the conclusion that the only other thing that could have made it was the pointed tip of a horn, either of a cheetal or of a young sambhar. Had either of these deer jumped down the steep bank and made a bad landing, hard though the ground was the hoofs of the animal would have broken the surface and left a track, but there were no deer tracks anywhere near the furrow. The final conclusion that I arrived at, therefore — with the furrow as my only clue — was that it had been made by the horn of a *dead* deer, and made when a tiger had jumped down the bank with the deer in its mouth. That there were no drag marks on the road was not unusual, for whenever it is possible to do so both tigers and leopards when crossing a road with a kill lift the kill clear of the ground, and this I believe they do to avoid leaving a scent trail for bears, hyaenas, and jackals to follow.

To test the accuracy of my deductions I crossed the road and looked down the hill on the left of the road. No drag marks were to be seen, but on a bush twenty feet down the hill and at a height of about four feet I saw something glistening on a leaf in the morning sun; on going down to investigate I found this was a big drop of blood, not yet quite dry. From here on, tracking was easy, and fifty yards farther down under the shelter of a small tree and surrounded by thick bushes I found the kill, a cheetal stag with horns that many a sportsman would have prized as a good trophy. The tiger was taking no chances of his kill — from which he had eaten both hind quarters — being found by bird or beast, for he had scratched together the dry leaves and twigs for a considerable distance round, and had heaped them on the kill. When a tiger does

this it is an indication that he is not lying up near by to keep an eye on the kill.

I had been told of a big tiger in this area which had been christened the Bachelor of Powalgarh. I had long wished to see this famous tiger that all the sportsmen in the province were trying to bag, and which I knew lived in a deep ravine that started near the sambhar wallow I was making for. As there were no pug marks near the kill by which I could identify the tiger that had killed the cheetal, it occurred to me that it was just possible that the kill was the property of the Bachelor and, if so, that there was now a reasonable chance of my having a look at this tiger to see if he was as big as he was reputed to be.

Starting from near the kill a narrow glade ran down to a small stream a hundred yards away. Beyond the stream was a dense patch of wild lime. If the Bachelor had not gone back to his ravine he would in all probability be lying up in this patch of cover, so I decided to try to get the tiger to return to his kill. Having come to this decision I went up towards the road and buried my white butterfly net under dead leaves. The glade at the upper end was about ten feet wide and the tree under which the kill was lying was about the same distance from the right-hand side of the glade. On the left-hand side, and nearly opposite the kill was the dead stump of a tree roofed over with creepers. First seeing that there were no holes in the dead stump to harbour snakes, I cleared away the dry leaves from the foot of the stump — to avoid sitting on scorpions — and then made myself comfortable with my back to the stump. From my seat I could see the kill, which was about thirty feet away, and I could also see down the glade to the stream, on the far side of which a troupe of red monkeys were feeding on the berries of a pipal tree.

When my preparations were completed, I gave the call of a leopard. Leopards will — when it is safe for them to do so — eat a tiger's kill, and of this tigers are very resentful. If the tiger was within hearing distance, and if my imitation was sufficiently good to deceive him, I expected him to come up the glade, and after I had had a good look at him I intended letting him know I was there and then make my getaway. The monkeys responded to my call by giving their alarm call, and three of them took up positions on a branch that jutted out from the pipal tree at right angles at a height of about forty feet above ground. The alarm call of the monkeys which, as they could not see me, only lasted for a minute or so was all to the good, for if the tiger was in the vicinity he would now be assured that a leopard was interfering with his kill. I kept my eye on the three monkeys, and presently I saw one of them turn round, peer into the jungle behind him, bob his head up and down several times, and then he gave an alarm call. A minute later the other two started calling and were followed by several others farther up the tree. The tiger was coming, and I greatly regretted not having my camera with me for he would make a grand picture, walking up the glade with the sun glinting on the water of the stream and the pipal tree with the excited monkeys on it in the background.

As usually happens on these occasions, however, the tiger did not do what I expected. After a long pause, during which I had the uneasy feeling that the tiger was approaching his kill from behind me, I caught a fleeting glimpse of him as he sprang across the stream and disappeared into the thick jungle on the right-hand side of the glade. After reconnoitering the position from the bushes beyond the stream the tiger had evidently concluded that if he came up the glade the leopard would see him, so he had started out to stalk the kill where he evidently expected to find the leopard. As far as I was concerned there was no objection to his doing this, though it would mean his coming closer to me than I had intended letting him.

236

The ground was carpeted with dry leaves, and the tiger accomplished his stalk without my hearing a sound. I next saw him as he was standing looking down at his kill but, to my great unease, I found I was not looking at the Bachelor, but at a big tigress. At the best of times a tigress's temper cannot be relied on, and this was not one of those "best of times", for I was sitting too close to her kill for my comfort, and, further, it was quite possible that she had cubs in the lime thicket, in which case she would resent my presence near her kill. However, if she went back the way she had come all would be well, but the tigress did not do this. After satisfying herself that the leopard had not touched her kill, she walked out on to the glade, halving the distance between us. For a long minute she stood

undecided, while I held my breath and closed my eyes until I was looking through a slit, and then she quietly walked down the glade, lay down at the stream, had a drink, and then sprang across the stream and disappeared into the thick cover . . .

I did not know, at the start, that a crime had been committed, and it is this uncertainty of not knowing what a small clue will lead up to that makes the compiling of jungle detective stories so interesting and so exciting.

Few can compile a detective story of fiction, but all can compile jungle detective stories provided they have eyes to see more than the road they walk on, and provided also that they do not start with the assumption that they know all, before in fact they know anything.